COUNTRY
& BYGONE

by Hamish Watt

Aberdeen Journals Ltd.

First published by
Aberdeen Journals Ltd., Lang Stracht,
Mastrick, Aberdeen AB9 8AF

ISBN 0 9510642 8 2

Printed by W. M. Bett, Tillicoultry

ABOUT THE AUTHOR

Hamish Watt is a Keith loon who got his education at the local school and at St Andrews University, where he studied Economics.

After three years as aircrew in the R.A.F. he commenced farming in the North-East and quickly became immersed in local affairs and in agricultural politics.

He entered the political field as a Conservative when he contested Caithness and Sutherland at the 1966 General Election. This experience fostered his abiding love of the North.

After switching allegiance to the Scottish National Party, he won the Banffshire seat in February and October 1974 and served at Westminster for five years, three of them as Whip.

His subsequent career in local politics at both district and regional levels, plus his farming activities meant frequent burning of the midnight oil. He found the Chairmanship of the Education Committee particularly challenging and rewarding.

Three years as Rector of Aberdeen University from 1986 led to him being awarded an honorary doctorate.

Early contributions to Farm Journal resulted in Hamish being allocated a weekly column where along with his great friend and rival, Charlie Allan, they share their wit and wisdom with Saturday readers.

FOREWORD

When Hamish Watt first approached me about writing a column for the Press and Journal I offered a word of caution. Many people, and farmers are no exception, think that writing is easy. Many have sound thoughts they wish to express but once some of their ideas have found expression, sustaining the writing proves more difficult and the well dries up.

It was probably the most unneccessary word of caution ever issued. Hamish Watt, one time Grampian regional councillor, former M.P. and farmer, began to contribute to the Farm Journal section of the P&J occasionally, then once every two weeks, eventually crossing the final barrier and going weekly. That was in 1989 and since then he has become an established, regular and consistent contributor.

Hamish Watt writes both as practical farmer, using his everyday background as material, but also as a keen observer of the farming industry and of life in general. He mixes contemporary events with historical antecedents, balances folklore and custom skilfully against the exigenoies of daily farming, and has in effect created a niche writing which appeals as much to urban readers of the P&J as to those in the vast rural hinterland.

Writing regularly as a columnist is of course a risky business because by its nature it exposes, week by week, article by article, the writer to his readers. In the process of revelation more of the writer becomes apparent. Success is illuminated, failure highlighted, doubts are flagged up and predelictions and prejudices are put under the spotlight.

Hamish Watt has allowed readers into his world and into his family — his grand daughter, dubbed Miss Bossy Boots — has become part and parcel of Watt's writings and an integral part of his rural chronicles. That, and his general approach, has only served to heighten his attraction and bring home the fact that the Watt style has struck a chord with many thousands of readers of his column and the P&J. The steady flow of letters received weekly by the farming desk of the P&J to be forwarded to Hamish Watt is testimony to his popularity.

The North-east and agriculture is the basis of Hamish Watt's writings but he has travelled further afield, to Beattock in the South west and to Caithness and Sutherland in the far North for material. He has written about dairy roups, sheep sales, big cats, recipes, superstitions, old cures, wolves, nicky tams and about the daily toil of making a living from the land. His emotions are tempered by the reality of farming today and in it there is none of the misty-eyed romanticism that has all too often dogged rural writing.

That is not to say it is writing without feeling for the land and the people that work it. It is a writing which oozes the countryside, its traditions, sights and sounds and smells, in short it is evocative and reflective.

Popular as his column has become it is not without its detractors and his views on pest control, for one, have not gone unchallenged. And from time to time his descriptions of the people he has known have caused sharp intakes of breath and not a few recriminations. That is, of course, is not only the stuff of a good column, but testimony to its attraction.

Hamish Watt has edited himself this collection of articles from the P&J published over the past few years. They represent his own choice of what he thinks best represent his style and contribution to the newspaper. They say a great deal not only about the author and his family but about an agricultural industry in transition with a long history and challenging and daunting future.

BILL HOWATSON
Agricultural Editor, The Press and Journal.

Black cat's return leads to an unlucky incident

Blackie was the friendliest and most affectionate kitten I ever possessed. Of course, nobody ever really possesses a cat, so I should say he was the friendliest kitten I ever knew.

He and his three litter mates were born in my hayshed among hundreds of big round bales, so they were quite well-grown by the time we saw them.

Accordingly, they escaped the cull that is often the fate of farm kittens if they are discovered before their eyes are open. A few cats to control vermin are fine — too many are a confounded nuisance.

The other three kittens were like their mother — grey and striped. Blackie, however, was jet black with not a trace of white or any other marking. The greys hissed and spat and scampered for cover whenever anyone approached. But Blackie was the exact opposite. He knew no fear and made a beeline for any human who came near his shed. He insisted in getting among your feet.

In no time at all, he had abandoned the nest and established living-quarters in the calf pens where the milk was always in plentiful supply. He would not allow anyone to ignore him, and stood in front of you until he got stroked.

His favourite pastime involved parading along the top of the pens, defying the calves to touch him with their noses. Any calf that made so bold got a cuff from Blackie's paw and by the way the calf sprang back, it was obvious he used his very sharp claws to gain mastery. One endearing way he used to get attention, if I was leaning forward into a calf pen, was to climb on my shoulder and lie against my neck like a fur collar. Then he would proceed to purr very loudly in my ear.

It must have been the regular supply of warm milk that made him grow so fast because he soon outgrew his siblings and was quite cock-of-the-walk.

Each summer, a pair of swallows nest high above the calf pens and rear one, sometimes two, broods. But not the year that Blackie reigned supreme. The kitten must have been ready to pounce whenever the fledglings left the nest. As well as small birds, small animals, such as voles, mice, young rats and young rabbits, were dragged back to the door of the shed to be partially devoured and quickly left for the older cats to finish off.

But damn't, there's aye something. That cat's toilet habits were disgusting and caused a great deal of trouble. He would cross the yard and do his business in the box that held the freshly-crushed oats and barley, fed to the cows twice a day. Cats have a strange habit of covering over their droppings, as anyone who has a cat and a litter tray will know. Anyway, if the polluted food went undetected, sure enough some poor cow would be very, very sick. It is small wonder that the worst character assassination

1

anyone can indulge in is to say of someone: "He is coorse as cat's dirt." I tried, and better than tried, to break him of the habit, but regardless of how many blows or kicks he got he didn't hold it against me and would be there as large as life next feeding time.

His first winter came and went and with the warmer spring weather Blackie would be missing for days at a time. Sometimes he came back the worse for wear, clear evidence that he had been fighting with something bigger or tougher than himself. But soon he would heal and off he would go again. Soon, he ceased coming back.

All of that was two years ago and I had almost forgotten the cat — that is, until a few days ago. It was one of those lovely October days when the sun is still warm in the middle of the day and I had just finished a long walk through the wintering lambs. There, coming out of the wood and slowly waving his tail in greeting was Blackie, mewing with pleasure. My dog obviously remembered him and slunk off to a discreet distance.

Blackie liked to have his ears fondled and he was quickly up on his favourite perch on my shoulder, purring away. Half of one ear was missing, but otherwise he was in great shape and his coat had a lovely sheen. The call of the wild had clearly agreed with him.

I was just about to take the cat from behind my neck when all of a sudden it dug its claws into me and stiffened. What had been as soft as velvet was now hard as sprung steel. Just below the bank on which I had been sitting was a narrow tarred road and Blackie had spotted a hare, three-quarters grown, coming towards us. The beast, all legs and ears, was completely oblivious to our presence.

Moving swiftly from my shoulder to the ground, the cat positioned itself at the edge of the bank to watch the hare's progress. The creature had just passed us when Blackie sprang into the air and pounced. The cat aimed perfectly and landed on the hare's back just behind its head. I've never seen such demonic fury anywhere else. That hare hardly knew what hit it. There was a short struggle, a few screams, and the poor brute lay kicking its last.

With never a backward glance to me, the ruthless killer dragged off the hare carcase, which was easily twice as big as himself. Doubtless, he would eat only a bit of it. Blackie obviously did not kill to live. He now lived to kill.

In the ring . . . the man

That's him!

The tall man in the centre of the ring, with the cloth cap and cool nerve. That is Willie Riddoch.

Take a good look at him, for you may not see his like again.

Mr Riddoch is the last of a long line of dairy cattle dealers operating in the North-east. It is good to see that he has made the transfer from the old Kittybrewster Mart to the new complex at Thainstone, Inverurie.

The new market has a lot to commend it and is well worthy of a visit by anyone who would like to witness a modern cattle market in operation. But keep your hands in your pocket or you might end up with a cow!

Sadly, the new market lay-out does not incorporate a byre where Mr Riddoch could display his wares to their full advantage. He likes to demonstrate the pliability of the skin over the animals ribs or the elasticity of the skin on the udder of his animals as he bids you a cheery "good morning and can I interest you in a real milk pump?"

The lovely animals are now kept loose in pens, but he still presents for potential buyers a wonderful show of big able Friesian cows and heifers each Thursday. They may represent good value for money but one thing is sure — they will not be cheap.

Each week he seeks to match supply with demand just as surely as any dealer or commodity broker on the London Stock Exchange. The London men handle stocks and shares while Mr Riddoch handles livestock which are liable to many types of risk.

It is a well-known fact that the only way not to have losses in livestock is not to keep any.

I must have been about eight years old when I was first introduced to the cattle market, when my father had to make the two-and-a-half hour trip from Keith to Aberdeen four times a year to replenish his dairy herd.

The smell of the market thrilled me just as much as the smell of a circus big top thrills other children. The aroma is a mixture of shampoo, sawdust and animal dung and I still enjoy it.

I have spent many happy days at dairy sales both as a buyer and seller. And I have enjoyed the company of the cattle dealers over the years. I can remember dealing with such men as Andy Brown, Johnnie Brown — no relation — Willie Waldie, Jimmy Low, Jack Wood and many others, and, for nigh on 50 years now, Willie Riddoch, all men whose eye was their merchant and their word their bond.

I lose patience with people who would scoff at cattle dealers as if they were a species to be avoided at all costs.

These men are only the honest brokers of supply and demand. They always provide a floor to a flagging sale and sellers are always grateful for their presence. They can sometimes annoy buyers on the other hand, because they ensure that no one gets a thief's bargain.

Dealers often act as discreet, unpaid, bankers to farmers who are hard up and there must be many times when Willie has to wait for his money till the farmers' monthly milk cheque comes through. Moreover, in cattle dealing, repeat orders are a must — so there is a lot of trust between seller and buyer.

Over the years the health of the cows being sold has improved dramatically as, first, tuberculosis and then brucellosis has been eliminated from our national dairy herd.

The past three years have seen a rapid decline in the numbers of dairy cattle being traded each week. Where now in the 90s there are only 10 cows each sale day, back in the 60s it was common to have more than 150 changing hands.

In the 60s there were 700 milk producers in Grampian — now there are 160.

The disappearance of the flying herds from the small farms around Aberdeen has led to the rapid decrease in cow numbers. No, young readers, flying herds did not have cows that circled around Dyce like helicopters do now, nor had they cows which jumped over the moon.

Flying herds were so called because the farmers bred no dairy replacements of their own. Their limited acreage meant that they kept only productive adult stock so these farmers were constantly in Aberdeen market looking for replacement cows.

Nowadays, most herds are closed, breeding and rearing all their own replacement stock. Many once-familiar faces are no longer seen around the dairy ring and hence Willie is always on the lookout for a potential new buyer. Alas, the cameraderie of the dairy ring has gone, also.

Willie, however, must still have his regular customers or he would not persist in the trade.

Although he has a good memory, he always consults his long slim diary about the details of each animal — and, after a short consultation with the auctioneer, the particulars are read out as to the number of days calved, or if uncalved, the breed of the bull which was used at mating.

He also announces whether she is a first or second calver — then off goes the bidding.

As in every auction, be it for furniture or antiques, old masters or livestock, each auctioneer has his own techniques and he sees bids where the onlooker sees only disinterested faces.

Anyway, from a modest start, the price rapidly climbs up to the point where Willie has to decide whether he will sell or not. If the price is right, Willie spreads his arms wide and calls "put her on the market, but take your time!" And so the animal reaches her final price and gets knocked down to the purchaser.

But it is the destination of the cows which do not reach their reserve price and are turned out of the ring unsold that provide the real mystique of cattle dealing. No amount of questioning of Willie will reveal the secret. The answer you will get will be: "You have to pay for your education in this business!"

I have to laugh when I speculate whether Willie's son, also William, decided not to follow in his father's footsteps (a) because the job of cattle dealing was too precarious or (b) because it was too staid.

Whichever way it was, William jun. decided that he wanted to be an actor. He regularly appears in films, TV and on the stage. That other Willie, Willie Shakespeare, claimed that all the world's a stage and men and women merely players.

Methinks Messrs Riddoch are more centre stage than most people — and each plays many parts.

Blackfaces offer mixed delights

The Blackies are back.

I suppose to lots of people a sheep is a sheep; but there is something extra special about the Blackface lambs.

Each October these lambs come tumbling off the lorry that has taken them from their home pastures in the hills of West Perthshire to the low ground of the Moray Coast. There they will spend the next six months of their life, grazing the stubble fields and the grass fields. They will build a bone structure and size that they will carry for the rest of their adult lives. If they are stocked too heavily their growth potential will be restricted. On the other hand, if they are stocked too lightly the farmer is losing income. A fine balance must be struck, therefore.

The arrival of the sheep marks the end of an intensive period of haggling over numbers of lambs to be wintered and the price to be paid by the owners of the flocks to the lowground farmer.

Their arrival also heralds the beginning of a love-hate relationshp between the farmer and the sheep. First of all, the lambs will object to being fenced in. Previously, the only bounds they have known since their birth in April have been a loch on one side and a mountain top on the other. Small wonder they do not take kindly to the petty restriction of a fence — especially if the grass looks greener on the other side.

This year the stubble grazing in the spring barley fields is providing adequate grazing and the mixture of weeds and natural grass is better for them when they first arrive. A diet of rich, heavily fertilised grass at this stage would cause them to scour, and that is something no sheepman wants. Scouring can occasionally lead to death and a dead sheep is no profit to either party.

Nevertheless, losses from one cause or another do occur and can be the source of friction between the two parties. So it is best to notify an outbreak of scour to the owners as early as possible.

When the owner first phones up the grazier to ask how the sheep are settling down, he will most certainly be told that there is "a gey lot of little anes among them. If you want me to send back elephants, why do you send down rabbits?"

The daily trek through the flock can vary from a pleasant walk on a fine, sunny autumn morning to sheer purgatory in the teeth of a February blizzard.

An animal can get caught in barbed wire or brambles. It will fiercely resist all attempts to disentangle it. Trying to grasp a piece of barbed wire from a sheep running past can lead to a very badly torn hand.

It is in these daily forays through the Blackies that you gradually get to know them. Blackface sheep have more distinctive markings than any other breed and are thus easier to recognise. I can well believe a shepherd who claims he knows every one of his flock of 500 ewes; but I think he would be stretched to identify each one of 800 or more.

First of all, you get to know the bonnie ones and the ugly ones. Then the Others fall into place — for example, a wanderer or a 'piner' is quickly recognised.

Having wintered Blackies for many years, I can readily understand the old Glenlivet flockmaster whose stock answer to the question of why he never married was: "Well, I never yet met a lassies that was as bonnie as a score of Blackface gimmers".

Bonnie these sheep certainly are, and this must be part of the reason why the same farmers winter the flocks from the same farm year after year. They could probably make more profit by buying and fattening sheep of their own. But the fact that no capital is tied up for six months must also be part of the attraction.

Moreover, it is sometimes possible to over-winter the Blackies with no supplementary feeding — especially if it is an open winter with little snow.

Hay has to be fed in times of deep snow or prolonged frost. But, provided a field of long-grass has been kept ungrazed, the sheep will often scrape down through the snow to the tuffets and totally ignore the bales of scattered hay. The digging process seems to make them stronger and it is often during a stormy time that you notice considerable growth.

The rabbits you have looked at for months suddenly show their potential. The sheep stand taller, the heads grow bigger and bonnier, and one or two shoot away above the rest.

The winds of March blow up their ample fleeces and the spring grass brings on the laggards. In the last fortnight of March the hoggs as they are now known (having changed from lambs to hoggs on January 1) become quite impossible to control.

The warm air of spring brings the smell of the mountain and they know, they just know, that it is time for them to return to their native hills.

The total count at loading on the last day of March is the vital one and will determine the size of the cheque the farmer receives for his bother.

There is real satisfaction and pride in sending back good sheep well wintered, knowing that they will produce a heavy wool clip in June and develop into strong gimmers by October, ready to breed and perpetuate the species. Right now, though, I wish they wouldn't send me rabbits.

Perfection needed for field work

Getting 100% isn't easy. In fact, it's dashed near impossible. Yet, there is one farm job where 99% just won't do.

I refer to fencing to hold in sheep. If even one wire is slack, a sheep will push and push until it gets its head and shoulders through. The whole body then slips through easily. Let one sheep get out and others will follow.

If they are to thrive well, sheep need a regular change of pasture, with preferably not more than 20 days in any one field. The biggest enemy any sheep has is another sheep.

This is true because worms and parasites constantly multiply where animals are closely herded together. These parasites have a 21-day life cycle, so it is more important to move the sheep on before they begin to ingest contaminated grass. If the parasite does not find a host, the cycle gets broken and the pests die off.

One field adequately fenced for sheep is clearly not enough. However, it is a laborius and expensive business to meet the ideal of having every field fenced properly.

With fence posts costing 94p at the last time of asking and every roll of wire setting you back £18, it is vital to repair and patch for as long as possible. Many sheep farmers now use rylock fencing, but we have yet to discover how resistant it is to the poking head of a persistent sheep.

If a contractor is employed to provide a new fence, the going rate is £2 a metre for posts at 7ft apart and six wires on the fence — three plain and three barbed. Incidentally, barbed wire was first introduced in the American West to separate one ranch from the next.

Where the fence must cross undulating ground, it is often necessary to add a seventh wire. A well-erected fence is a source of great satisfaction; and it is certainly a relief to know that the sheep will stay where they are meant to be.

The grass is always greener on the other side and the little hill lambs we rear and finish have never known restriction. With a loch on one side and a mountain on the other, they have been free to roam with their mothers where fancy takes them. When transported to a lowland farm, the lambs must learn to stay within limits. Most settle down well, but there is always the rogue that tries your patience and your fences.

To most people, a fence is a fence. To those who know better, a fence is either a work of art or a botched job. At the cost of around £2,000 a field, it would be grand if they were all works of art — and lasted as long as an old master!

Every fence needs major attention at least every seven years and total renewal after 14 years. This timespan is stretching however, now that posts are celcurised, that is, treated with wood preservative under pressure.

Since the fence has to remain rigid and taut for such a lengthy time, good strainer posts are absolutely essential. These big, heavy posts are some 9in in diameter. To secure half the length of a post underground, a deep hole must be dug and the post packed at the heel with a big stone or concrete block.

Another concrete block just below ground level at the other side — the ankle, as some people call it — ensures that it will stand the terrific strain of six wires pulled tight.

Tractor-mounted drivers which force the posts into the ground have taken some of the hard work out of fencing. Before this practice was developed, all posts were hammer driven by a 12lb mell with a stout man at the end of the stout shaft.

For many years, I had a great grieve who was a real enthusiast for fencing. One cold November day he came into the cow byre with blood streaming from the top of his head. He had been holding a post steady while Jimmy, the orraman, chapped it in. Suddenly, the head of the mell flew off, stunning the grieve and opening a bad gash on his crown.

Jimmy, unfortunately, was the most feckless chiel we ever employed. He had endured rough times as a prisoner of war after capture at St Valery. A long convalescence followed his release, but he never regained his full strength and was aye fushionless.

A good orraman was, of course, worth his weight in gold around a farm in past times. The best of them could turn their hand competently to a wide variety of tasks. Sadly, Jimmy never measured up. One hay day, the grieve came up to me in a rage, saying that Jimmy was worse than useless on the seat of the mower. "I wid be better wi' his photo on the seat", he said. "Well, sack him and find somebody else", I replied. But he never did. He couldn't harden his heart.

There was great rejoicing about the ferm toon when some months later Jimmy announced he was leaving to work on a building site.

We replaced him with a tractor-mounted dung loader and had a happier squad as a result.

Wild goose chase

There are few sights more thrilling to a country lover than the magnificent spectacle of skein after skein of wild geese crossing the evening sky. But should these birds happen to land on your field of newly-established young grass the delight can quickly turn to anger.

Until fairly recently, the geese were seen flying south only in late autumn to their wintering grounds in the Forth and Tay Valleys. The island of Islay with its mild climate is a favourite haunt for various species of overwintering flocks, and the extensive marshes and tidal creeks of the Solway Firth see an annual invasion which is as deeply detested by farmers as it used to be welcomed by shooters.

In spring, the arrival of warmer weather was traditionally heralded by the sight of the surviving geese flying north on the first stage of their long flight to the breeding grounds in Iceland and the Arctic.

Over the past two years, however, things have changed dramatically. Now, instead of birds flying south and north only twice yearly, there are vast flocks moving in all directions every day. What was once a rarity is now a daily spectacle.

Motorists can frequently catch a glimpse of geese pulling at the plants of young grass and clover. Recently, I have watched flocks in excess of five thousand birds in the Saphook district of Oldmeldrum; and I have seen even larger numbers in the Buckie/Deskford area.

Twice now, I have taken the time to gauge totals by counting the geese in one leg of the arrow formation and doubling the number. By counting the skeins as they wing in to land and multiplying the two numbers, an acurate total can be arrived at. I wonder if professional birdwatchers would care to confirm or dispute my figures — or do they prefer not to see the problem?

At this time of year, the birds are competing with sheep flocks for scarce winter fodder. I am no birdwatcher — having never found the time — but it appears that the geese, in their wisdom, like to graze in the same fields as sheep. Perhaps they realise that they are less likely to be shot at or disturbed in such company.

As it is estimated that six geese eat as much grass as one sheep, the farmers who experience a daily visitation of the birds have a very real problem on their hands. The geese will clear off when the grass is finished and fly to another farm in the neighbourhood, but the poor sheep are left to face starvation with no alternative food supply.

About 10 years ago, the Royal Society for the Protection of Birds successfully pressurised Parliament to pass legislation which afforded blanket protection to all species of geese. And with the total prohibition of shooting there has been, inevitably, a vast increase in numbers. This population explosion has yearly gone unchecked until there now exists a situation whereby geese numbers are rapidly outstripping the food supply both in summer and winter.

Driving back south from lamb sales at Forsinard in the second week of August, I was horrified to observe about two hundred land in the Helmsdale river close by the road. These had returned 10 weeks earlier than usual. In their summer breeding grounds, the geese have few natural enemies and each breeding female rears five or six goslings. Obviously, the numbers progression would make a mathematician's hair turn grey.

Sheer pressure of numbers on the traditional feeding grounds are forcing the birds ever farther north to overwinter in areas such as Grampian. During open winters, like those of the last two years, they can survive. But the next really hard winter, with the grass deeply covered by snow, will see the death through starvation of many thousands of birds.

Doubtless, in desperation, they will turn to the crops of winter barley, winter wheat and maybe even winter rape. The lucky farmers will be those whose crops are completely buried by snow. But woe betide the coastal farmer when his snow cover melts. No amount of bird-scareres will deter ravenous geese.

When, not if, we get three solid weeks of deep snow with no alternative food supply, who is going to tackle the problem of burying the wasted carcases? Will the members of the RSPB face up to the consequences of their action, or will it be left to the farmer upon whose land they happen to die? There are no prizes for the correct answer.

Perhaps the National Farmers' Union ought to disband, reform as the Society fo the Protection of Farmers, and then seek Royal patronage. The members of the new RSPF would get at least as much sympathy from the general public as does the NFU at present. But I would hazard a guess that the bird society would continue to receive the donations.

It is a great pity that Governments, regardless of their political colour, never get things right. They always over-react or act in isolation. A positive, commonsense approach is urgently needed. One possible solution for feeding the geese would be for the EEC to instruct those farmers who have opted for set-aside to sow clover in their bare fields. The birds would quickly recognise a sanctuary with the right kind of feed.

Most importantly, however, the bird protection lobby can no longer be allowed to shrug off their responsibility for the present situation and the impending disaster. Legislation must be amended to allow a reasonable cull of the geese flocks, thus ensuring that numbers will more closely equate to available food supply.

Fortunately, there are still sufficient sportsmen around who would participate in such a cull. And there are plenty trigger-happy Europeans eager to pay for the privilege of a few days shooting. The birds appear to be in beautiful condition right now; and a succulent wild goose is a worthy substitute for a dry Christmas turkey.

That said, count me out when the shooting starts. My gun is strictly reserved for the marauding dogs that periodically seek to cull my sheep flock. And besides — I like wild geese — in reasonable numbers and preferably Not In My Back Yard.

One man's dedication

It is always pleasant to see in the Press and Journal photographs of long-serving farm employees being presented with an award from the Royal Highland and Agricultural Society. Often, the man will have served the same employer for 35 years or more.

Now, there is one individual who has served North-east agricultural interests for twice as long as that, yet his contribution goes unrecognised. For more than 70 years, Mr John Kelly, wholesale butcher extraordinary, has faithfully attended our local auction marts, playing a vital role in underpinning the prosperity of our beef trade.

It all started back in 1920 when an English buyer (an acquaintance of his father) invited the young John Kelly to accompany him on a day trip to Aberdeen mart. That initial foray into unknown territory laid the basis for the establishment of a trading connection that has continued unbroken to the present day. And all North-east farmers must certainly hope that the firm of J. Kelly and Son, Larkhall, near Hamilton, will long continue to flourish in its specialist cow-beef sector.

Over the years, many individuals and companies have started up in buying and manufacturing cow beef, but one after another they have blossomed and withered. Only J. Kelly and Son has stood the pace; and today, at the age of 85, John Kelly can be seen every Friday afternoon gracing the ringside at the new Thainstone mart complex.

Dairy cows, hill cows, fat cows, thin cows and heifers — all are sought after to satisfy heavy customer demand for mince and pie meat in Central and West Scotland. Unlike many of the now defunct companies that once were household names in the trade, Messrs Kelly stuck to supplying local customers and did not venture into the more lucrative but also highly volatile foreign markets.

A quiet-spoken, modest man is Mr Kelly, a man who knows what he wants and means what he says. Not for him the worry of the sterling exchange rate against the franc, the deutschmark or the guilder. The bill for his purchases from Aberdeen and Northern Marts is settled every mart day, and in turn farmers can have their cheques home with them shortly after their cows have been sold.

Some 60% of all beef cattle are sold direct from farm to meat packer. Under this system the farmer has to wait up to 21 days for his cheque. But cattle sold through the auction markets are paid for on the day of the sale. For this reason alone, many farmers prefer to submit their stock to auction. An added bonus is that the seller can say "No" and take his animals home if he is dissatisfied with the price being offered.

Although one system does at times gain a larger proportion of the throughput than the other, I hope the two methods continue to co-exist, leaving seller and buyer an element of choice in an increasingly monopolistic society.

Talking of choice, back on that Saturday in 1920 it was not to Kittybrewster mart, or the Central mart, or even to the Belmont mart that young Mr Kelly and his English friend were bound. Their destination was Duncan's mart, in King Street, situated in the quadrant across Nelson Street from the Pittodrie Bar. One can only speculate on the scenes in King Street when farmers were celebrating a good sale or drowning their sorrows over a poor one. And things must have been especially lively when the farming fraternity met up with football fans on their way to a match!

In those days, buyers and sellers had ample choice of marts and mart days. Although I started attending Aberdeen markets as a laddie in short trousers during the late 1930s, I never knew of Duncan's mart. It will need a voice from an earlier generation than mine to describe it. Donald Henderson, of Kintore, who must be about the same age as John Kelly, tells me that all cows at Duncan's mart were chained up so that the buyer could poke and prod and assess accurately each animals degree of finish.

At auction the cows fetched from £2 to £10, with an exceptional beast reaching £15. That price level pertained from 1920 until 1940. There was virtually no inflation then. In fact, if anything there was slight deflation. A cow that realised £15 in 1920 would have fetched £600 in 1990. However, with the loss of the German market following the BSE scare, that same animal would now bring in only £450 — a drop of 25% on last year.

Mr Kelly assures me that the quality of cows presented at market has improved throughout the years. The introduction of the Freisian breed from Friesland in 1922 has done much to improve the size of the average dairy cow. More recently, the arrival of the Continentals — Charolais, Simmental and Limousin — has had a similar effect on the beef breeds. Yet it must be said that only these three newcomers have had any real influence on our beef herds. Attempts to introduce many other exotic breeds, including Chianina, Belgian Blue and Romagnola, have by and large failed.

When Scotland was still an industrial nation in the 50s and 60s, Messrs Kelly used to require 300 cows per week. Some of their customers, such as Coal Board canteens, actually bought mince by the ton. Today, a throughput of 120 to 150 cattle and 300 sheep, keeps himself and his able lieutenant, nephew Mr Ian Gemmell, really busy.

John Kelly has always believed in prompt payment and prompt collection of debts. He deplores the present trend of some supermarket chains to delay payment of invoices for up to 60 days. He prefers to turn down that kind of business, rather than carry the risk of heavy interest charges.

As well as buying stock at auction, Messrs Kelly provide a unique farm collection service. For those farmers who prefer to sell their cattle and sheep privately off the field, Mr Gemmel will call and buy direct. One of the firm's seven lorries will subsequently uplift the animals within one week.

John Kelly really is a stoical man because in all weathers and conditions he travels by train each Friday morning from Glasgow to Aberdeen. On arrival, he meets up with his nephew who will already have spent three days in the North, buying privately. They return south after the sale in the comfort of a fast car.

Together, these two work fantastically-long hours and provide a wonderful service to North-east farmers. Proof of their prudent business methods lies in the fact that their company has survived many booms and slumps in what has always been a precarious trade.

Mr Kelly would be the last person to seek recognition or tribute for just doing what he regards as his job. But time — especially 71 years of it —adds a certain aura to the most humdrum of tasks. I think the appropriate phrase here is dedication to the job.

John Kelly — we salute you and give you our grateful thanks for that dedication. Long may the name of Kelly appear on the selling slips of the customers who attend Aberdeen and Northern Marts.

Sad farewell to an old friend

I said goodbye to an old friend the other day — an acquaintance of 12 or 13 years of whom I was very fond.

Like Katie Bairdie's coo, she was black and white about the moo — a combination of colour that always made her distinguishable among 150 other dairy cows. Besides, she had another endearing factor. She would never pass me without saying hello and waiting for a clap and a cuddle. To other people she paid no attention; just she and I were buddies.

Quite often, bucket-reared calves become friendly but after joining the herd they usually forget their handler. However, Glove never forgot me, even although she might only see me four times in a fortnight when it was my weekend at the milking.

Isla Glove III — that was her official title registered in the British Friesian Society Herdbook. This showed she was the third daughter of a cow called Glove that I had bought at the dispersal sale of Sir Charles Clore's dairy herd at Hungerford.

I remember that sale well — in a lovely part of Berkshire on a lovely day; and the herd the finest I have ever seen dispersed. Perhaps what was even more memorable was the fact that the cows were not too expensive, or as we say in the cattle trade: "I got them at my own money." Nobody forgets a bargain.

The Glove family have proved long-lived and prolific breeders of females. I now have three daughters and several grand-daughters in the herd. The most recent registration was Isla Glove 321, which identifies the calf as the first daughter of Glove 32, which in turn was the second daughter of my old favourite.

The average productive life of a dairy cow in Britain is 2½ lactations, so Glove with her eight lactations was exceptional.

There are six other cows of the same vintage in the herd, and alas, all will have to go shortly. To keep them much longer is just courting trouble as the hard life of a dairy cow is quite stressful. They become prone to difficult calving, prolapses, milk fevers and so forth.

Glove, I am pleased to say, had suffered only one illness and made a marvellous recovery. Her teat placement and udder attachment would have done credit to many cows half her age.

She walked smartly round the farrow ring at the mart on straight legs and beautiful feet like a ballet dancer. The feet of most cows in the cubicle and parlour system grow long and misshapen and need chiropody once or twice a year to trim off excess growth of hoof.

Foot trimming is hard and dangerous work and rates along with turnip pulling as a disagreeable occupation. You get extremely tense in case you hurt the cow — or the cow hurts you.

Had Glove been a beef instead of a dairy cow, she could probably have lived and produced longer — perhaps for another four to six years.

Beef cows lead less stressful lives, rearing as they do only one calf and benefitting from long rest periods. My bonnie lass calved regularly every year within a 365-day calving index, and rarely had more than five weeks of a dry period before calving again.

The farrow cows ring at the old Belmont was a fascinating place where animals of all shapes, sizes and breeds wer sold to their final home — the meat market and the pie trade.

The auctioneer, Mr Ronnie Walker, sold two animals per minute and at busy sales in the autumn could sell 500 and more on a Friday afternoon without taking a break — and only a cup of tea for sustenance.

There were rarely more than eight buyers round the ring and he knew which animal suited which buyer. He always started the bidding as high as possible to save himself unnecessary talking.

Glove started at £480 and sold out at £552. It was not your fault you hit a bad day, lass. The latest change in MCA's has meant a drop of £50-60 in recent weeks.

My long-time friend and acquaintance, Mr John Kelly of Hamilton, bought my cow, which meant she had to travel only to Strathclyde. Had she been bought by one of the Continental buyers, she might have faced a much longer journey.

Mr Kelly — now in his eighties — has been a stalwart attender at Friday marts since the 1920's and is himself worthy of a newspaper article. I only hope he follows the mart to its new premises at Thainstone.

The farrow ring or cast ring or rough ring or jing-a-ring as it was affectionately known, has developed a language of its own. It is rather similar to Cockney slang. Thus, when Mr Kelly bought Glove, the animal handlers shouted out "Bingo" — that is, Kelly — Kelly's eye — "Bingo"!

Similarly, Mr Bell is known as Ting-a-ling and Mr Batchelor as Lucky Man! Such cries identify the pen in which the animals must be collected and grouped for their overnight journey. Glove had a good feed before she left the farm in the morning, and water is always provided.

As the cattle leave the ring, they pass through a cattle crush where a yardsman expertly gives them a scissor mark on their plate or hip. A different mark is allocated for each buyer so mistakes are few, despite the speed of throughput and the general hubbub.

I see from her record-sheet that Glove's heifer calves were all by artificial Insemination. My son, Michael, and I both learned the technique of insemination on the same two-day course and we have vied since to see who can achieve the best conception rates.

I can well remember our first attempts before we got the hang of inserting that plastic rod with its straw of semen carefully into the right spot of the uterus. Old cows came easy, but the first-time heifers were "fickle" — indeed, they still are. Glove must have been one of those poor animals that had to put up with our early clumsy attempts.

Her last two calves were by that handsome Frenchman, the Limousin bull whose name I never did learn. I managed to buy him canny because he had a slight limp in a front leg, but not one of his hundreds of partners objected to his infirmity one little bit.

He throws beautiful big, strong calves with plenty of bone about them; yet seldom have they given difficulty in calving. The enhanced price that his progeny have fetched has helped to balance the farm books in these times of crippling interest rates. Thank God for cattle of quality and character.

"Well, so long, Glove, old lass. An interesting, productive life and a swift and painfree end is all that any of us can aspire to."

Goodbye, or as they say at Buckie: "See you later." And if you do see me later, maybe it will be your turn to put me in a lorry and see me through a jing-a-ring.

Spring hopes, eternal

There are lots of ladies-in-waiting around this spring — more than I've ever seen before.

In field after field they stand, dignified and stout, a few days or weeks from lambing.

The open winter has ensured that lambing ewes have come through in good condition; and should the weather hold reasonable for the next six weeks there may well be a record lamb crop.

Department of Agriculture statistics show only a modest increase in the number of breeding ewes in Scotland this year. My travels tell me a different story. Journeying through Grampian, even the casual observer might notice more flocks of in-lamb ewes on our farms than in years past.

There the lovely ladies stand — Suffolk crosses, Greyfaces, Halfbreds, Cheviots — all in the later stages of pregnancy. Further up country, on hill and upland farms, the Blackfaces are not due till April.

I never did find out why most farmers aim to start the lambing on March 20, but I would hazard a guess that 50% or more of all lowland flocks put up their tups in on October 20.

As they near the delivery date the ewes become very reluctant to take exercise, yet this is essential if they are to keep fit.

Many farmers deliberately feed turnips in one field and hay and trough feed in another, forcing the ewes at least to move between fields. Only after lambing has relieved them of their burden will they again forage for a blade of fresh grass to help boost the milk supply. But in the meantime, there they are — all standing waiting.

I travel around the side roads of Grampian a great deal, having inherited from my mother a dislike of leaving home and then returning by the same route. And just as I see ewe flocks managed under different regimes, I also see the prospective midwives keeping an eye on the prospective patients.

This attention tends to follow a pattern — farmer in the morning, farmer's wife during the day, and the farmer again at dusk, walking quietly through the flock checking that all is well. If you were to ask they would deny it, but I know that all of them — farmers and wives — are itching to get going.

As they walk round the sheep, they are thinking that this is going to be the year when lambing goes well.

Plenty of twins and just enough triplets to provide one for mothering on to the ewe which drops a single. Every day a dry day with some sun on the young lambs' backs to get them "roaded". This is going to be the year when lambing reaches 175%, maybe even 180%.

The grass is going to grow early and the ewes will all lamb down with plenty of milk to make a good job of twins. And there will be little mismothering. Aye well, if you didn't dream sometimes you wouldn't farm for a living.

Sadly, reality is very different.

The first few ewes which give birth before their due date often produce dead lambs. Then come those with big single lambs — so big, indeed, that they often get stuck.

A ewe that was all right when seen by torchlight at 11 p.m. can, by 5 a.m., have the lamb's head sticking out but no feet showing.

If the lamb has been in that position for several hours it is extremely difficult to push the head back inside in order to find the feet. But find them you must, and then pull forward gently, front feet and head together. If luck is with you the lamb will still have life. It must be persuaded to breath by slapping, working the tongue backwards and forwards, or swinging it round your head to drive air into the lungs. When it finally draws breath the tongue must be massaged until it is sufficiently soft to enable the lamb to suck its mother.

All this time you must ensure that the ewe does not get up and run away.

You take her teat between finger and thumb and squirt the first milk, or colostrum, into the lamb's mouth. Colostrum is the nearest thing to elixer of life. Once the lamb has swallowed a few mouthfulls life literally flows into it.

Within minutes, it struggles to its feet and comes poking at its mother's udder. But watch, before you allow the ewe to stand up, take the trouble to insert your hand well inside her because there might just be another lamb waiting to be born. To turn a potential disaster into a pair of well suckled lambs is part of the art of good shepherding and brings a deep feeling of satisfaction.

The first seven to 10 days of lambing are often slow, making it the ideal time to initiate a keen youngster into the mysteries of the job.

As in any trade, a new apprentice is a liability. But if the boy or girl even acts as a 'gate' then that's some help.

The youngster is invariably fleeter than the farmer or his wife and quickly learns to catch ewes — although learning how to turn them over takes considerably longer.

A young person who shows interest in the job will always appreciate an encouraging word at mealtimes. After a few days' busy lambing, farmhouse conversation becomes one long saga of this ewe and that lamb, this success and that failure. At least one extra person (preferably not family) is vital at lambing time. That individual gives the farmer someone other than his wife to shout at, someone other than his dog to swear at!

By the third week, the lambs are coming thick and fast and there are plenty opportunities for shouting and swearing.

Weather deteriorates and so do tempers. Try going out at first light on a frosty morning and discovering a bonny gimmer with two tup lambs frozen to the ground. You may feel like crying but you are better to swear. The ewe has an udder full of milk and a spare lamb must be found to mother on. Get on with it.

Try going out to the flock and finding a ewe with three lambs milling around her. Two other ewes hover close by, darting in and out, trying to pinch a lamb. Sorting that lot out is no task for an amateur.

Careful examination will probably reveal that the hovering ewes are the real mothers of twins and a single.

Then you discover that the sheep doing the baby-snatching has not yet lambed.

If isolated from the melee, she will soon settle down to producing her own lambs. Meanwhile, you will be lucky if the robbed ewes accept their offspring back.

From scenes like these does sheer frustration spring.

That ewe away by herself has been pressing for a long time. You investigate and find only a tail showing with two hips firmly wedged in the pin bones.

A good shepherd does more pushing back than pulling out. Another ewe has three feet showing and no head to be felt anywhere. Push back again until you can get your hand in, tickle a head forward with the tips of your fingers, get two feet forward into the passage and pray that the head and the two feet belong to the same lamb. If not, push back again and try another permutation.

By the fourth week all euphoria has gone.

Fatigue has set in through prolonged lack of sleep and constant walking. You have to be on the move morning, noon and night and every minute in between.

Then, without your actually noticing, it arrives — the day when there are more ewes in the lambed field than in the maternity ward. And two weeks later the end is in sight, with only a handful of stragglers left to lamb.

The chances are that half of these will produce no offspring. They are either barren (tup eild) or will have have cast their lambs prior to lambing. Their looks are deceptive because they are in prime fat condition. They will best be despatched to market and the mutton pie trade.

And who am I? I'm just the passing motorist who knows what you are thinking.

Good luck, and good lambing!

Ruthless killer learns new tricks

I never liked crows much. Now, I detest them.

Over the years, the crow has changed character — changed from a marauder to a ruthless killer. As a struggling farmer in the 50s, I used to dread the crows attacking the heads of my corn ricks during a hard winter and letting the water in.

However, the numbers of crows around then were such that they could be stopped by nets or bird-scarers strung between the rows. And a tethered crow was the best bird-scarer of all.

Today, crow numbers have exploded to the extent that they are in danger of becoming a totally dominant species.

I recently had occasion to pass through a rookery or crow wood and was quite appalled at the stinking white hell I experienced there. There was barely room for the birds to perch, let alone find space to build a nest.

Dead and dying birds were littered everywhere. It is small wonder the colonies of crows now establish rookeries in woodland unsuitable to the purpose and build nests in species of trees where no crow nest was ever known before.

But my principal reason for disliking crows is the way they seek to destroy so many other birds and animals. I have always been sceptical of shepherds' claims that crows will peck out the eyes of living lambs; but nowadays I am inclined to believe it when I see just how vicious the crow has become.

Early this year, I was spreading muck from the cow cubicles straight on to a stubble field. Following the spreader were hundreds of small birds — thrushes, starlings, blackbirds, finches — all anxious to get at the particles of broken barley and the weed seeds being showered on to the ground.

Very soon, the scene was dominated by crows which were there not only for the scraps but also with the intention of killing smaller birds in the melee. In the space of ten minutes I saw at least eight small birds battered to the ground by the wings of crows. Clearly, they were operating in pairs. When the unfortunate little birds fell hurt, they were pounced upon by at least two crows on the ground and quickly torn to pieces with their beaks.

It was obvious from the accuracy of their attacks that the crows had used such tactics before. Late winter and early spring are the times for scattering the bags of small corn and weed seeds collected from beneath the grain dresser at harvest. Many farmers actively ensure that the smaller birds get this food in a snowy period when little other sustenance is available. But unless there are thick bushes to protect these birds while they eat, they fall easy victim to crows practising dive-bombing techniques.

Although no particularly enthusiastic tractorman, I do occasionally get pressed into jobs like breaking in the ground before sowing and harrowing or rolling the land after the combine drill. Straightforward driving of this kind provides ample opportunity to observe wildlife at close hand.

For several springs now, I have seen crows ripping up the nests of brown hares and devouring leverets in their first few days of life.

As the adult female normally has two nests some distance apart, with half the litter in each, she has no way of extending complete protection at all times. The wily crow can bide its time.

Moreover, I have become convinced that crows are mainly responsible for the dramatic fall in the numbers of moorland birds such as grouse and blackcock — although other factors like excessive heather burning or overstocking with sheep often get blamed for the scarcity.

Indeed, all ground-nesting birds — pheasant, partridge, lapwing and curlew, for example — are equally at risk from the crow's predations. Unless something is done by man to restore the balance, we may soon reach a point where crows and seagulls dominate the rural scene.

For some unexplained reason, during the space of my lifetime rural man has abdicated his role as the guardian of the balance of nature.

Consequently, the crow population has multiplied at least tenfold in the past 30 years. Throughout the year, Crow Raid Societies used to hold well attended dances, whists and concerts to raise funds for the purchase of cartridges and bullets and for the remuneration of the raiders whose task it would be to climb the trees and plunder the nests for eggs and young crows.

The raiders were young lads from surrounding districts who eagerly cycled miles to the crow wood in order to earn a few shillings.

For me, no spring would have been complete without my three forays to the woods of Tarryblake. Edingight and Edintore in the Keith area. Memory does not recall whether a different pair of trousers was required on each occasion, or whether running repairs were effected between each raid.

My mother never scolded much: she regarded the stitches as her contribution to maintaining the balance of nature. My brothers and I were keenly encouraged to take part in the cull. Money was not exactly the spur. Certainly, at the going rate of tuppence for an egg and fourpence for a crow, no fortunes were made.

I can well recollect the shock of my first introduction to a crow raid.

Arriving for a six o'clock start, my partner and I gave our names to the tallyman who was to keep our joint score. Then we were allocated to a ladderman who told us which tree to climb. He waited only until one of us had reached the first branch of the tree and then promptly walked off with the ladder! It was subsequently the climber's task to shin out almost to the end of the branches (the nests were generally built there) and to collect the eggs by dropping them gently to his partner. Needless to say, breakages were high — and yolk up your sleeve is horrible.

You then dislodged any young crows still on the branch. As they fluttered down they were caught by your partner and despatched with a swift smack on the head. These were then collected in a pile, a good tree yielding 20 crows and 40 eggs.

Finally, there came the difficult part when you had to shin down the rough tree trunk as best you could. This was the manoeuvre that played havoc with the trousers: and oh, how I envied the older lads with long trousers!

After the catch was gathered and delivered to the tallyman, we had to find the ladderman who, by this time, had moved to another part of the wood. The next tree was your partners responsibility and so we took turn about, climbing and collecting until darkness fell. If a young crow fluttered out of reach, you called on a nearby shooter with a small-bore rifle to shoot it out of the tree. And so, collectively, man and boy, we controlled the crow population for another year. No carcases were left to cause disease carryover.

There was great camaraderie in the crow wood and even better camaraderie on the long cycle home with your earnings tucked into the top jacket pocket — the only pocket left without a hole in it.

Whether our role was that of criminal or curator, we lads enjoyed it. And. most importantly, the surviving crows had a space to enjoy a reasonable form of life and a food supply more closely matched to their numbers.

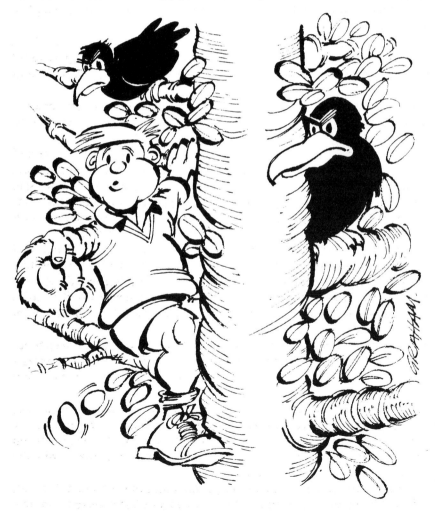

New-found efficiency cost us the best of friends . . .

The other Saturday, I jinked off from the afternoon milking to watch the Grand National. By the time I had removed my smelly wellies and switched on the telly the horses were at Beecher's Brook the second time round. The leader had stumbled so badly that the jockey was thrown off over his neck. A grey horse following saw the man on the ground and while still in mid air, swerved violently to avoid him.

The twisting action, which must have hurt the grey, sent my mind back to a similar response by a horse I knew very many years ago.

Prince wasn't a big horse. As vanners go, he was really quite small — about the size of a Highland garron, I would say. That would have made him 14 hands high. Unlike a garron, however, Prince was short coupled, with a short back and therefore a fairly short stride.

I can remember that he was bouncy to ride bareback and not nearly as pleasant as some of our horses with a longer stride. His step at times betrayed a touch of hackney in his ancestry, and his stance was erect and proud.

Prince was bought to be number three in our team of milk cart horses in the spring of 1940, when my father had just lost two of his best vanners to grass sickness.

It seems almost incredible that now, in the 1990s, veterinary science still has not found a cure for a disease that yearly claims so many fine horses. A friend of mine lost three ponies within one week last June. With hindsight, we can well understand why farmers quickly changed from horse to tractor power in the face of appalling losses each spring. But no tractor on earth will ever have the attraction of a well trained and willing horse.

Despite strict war-time rationing of petrol, the local butcher had acquired an old van for his country round, and we were grateful to buy from him a replacement horse which was already familiar with the town of Keith. More importantly, Prince was a mature animal and less likely to be struck down with grass sickness since this malady always seemed to be at its most deadly among younger horses.

Although rather light in the body for pulling heavy loads up steep braes on the way to town, Prince was very willing and had impeccable manners. I have known more affectionate horses than he. He kept himself aloof; but he never bit the hand that fed him.

Many people who are now grandparents have fond childhood memories of giving Prince a "piece" as he passed their mother's doors on his daily milk round. His coat was a beautiful red chestnut and had a gloss on it even on a cold winter's day. The colour could most nearly be compared with the autumn coat of the red squirrel.

Working with some horses was a constant battle of wills, but not so with Prince. My father, who wouldn't have hurt a fly unless it kicked him first, instantly took to this good-natured, obedient workmate. They formed a bond that lasted seven years, through good days and bad, in all weathers.

Motor vehicles were very scarce on the civilian front in the early war years and it was relatively safe for children to sledge on the side streets of Keith. One particular stretch, known as Jessiman's Brae, was, in any event, too steep for the cars of the day; and generations of bairns had found it an ideal place for high speed sledging. The gradient was such that once a sledge set off from the top there was no hope of stopping or regaining control until it reached level ground at the bottom.

In the street at the top of the brae lived a family with three little boys — daredevil twins of five and their three-year-old brother — while immediately at the bottom a small cul-de-sac contained the houses of four of our customers. High stone walls ran along the length of the brae on both sides, completely blocking the vision of the youngsters who played there.

One winter, when the snow cover was just right for fast sledging, the inevitable happened: with one of the twins lying flat on a sledge and his young brother sitting erect on his back, the pair set off down the brae at the very time our horse was emerging from the cul-de-sac and positioned at right angles to the brae.

My father pulled the reins and Prince halted in his usual excellent posture — front two feet together and back two together. Any other arrangement of the feet and legs would have meant instant disaster but the boys, who were not in control of their sledge, shot right underneath the horse's belly, miraculously missing both front and hind legs. The sledge was 15in. wide, the distance between front and hind legs 32in. I reckon the sledge was travelling around 20 miles an hour.

The terrified boys fell off unhurt a few yards farther on.

My father got such a fright that he was violently sick and could not be persuaded to take the horse's reins for the remainder of the day.

Had the sledge gone to the left, in front of Prince, it would have crashed into the wall. Had it gone to the right, behind Prince, the lads would have hit the wheel of the milk float. They do say there is a special God for drunk men and little boys. He was certainly on duty that day. The whole thing happened so quickly, but I often relive the experience and shudder.

Nobody knew Prince's exact age, but over the years he allowed a whole succession of young lads to harness him, drive him and ride on his back to and from the fields — without saddles, of course. That was the only riding ever allowed on our farm because the horses were there for work, not as playthings.

On one leave just before I was demobbed from the RAF in 1947 I brought back a pal from London who had never been on a horse's back before. As Prince was the most reliable, I helped my friend to mount and then jumped on to my own mare. All went reasonably well for the first part of the ride.

However, as Prince neared the field a tasty meal of fresh grass clearly came uppermost in his mind and he broke into a trot. My airman friend fell on to the horse's neck and clinging to the mane, hung for a few seconds in front of the running horse and then dropped to the ground.

Prince, with a twisting action even more violent than that of the grey in the Grand National, flung himself desperately to the side, reared and fell heavily backwards rather than tread on his rider. By his swift action he had again avoided human tragedy.

Sadly, Prince twisted his back so badly that he never really recovered and was so obviously in pain that I had to say goodbye to yet another old friend.

There is a saying that good horses and good dogs never live long enough. I also happen to believe the same applies to good folk.

To take by the hand . . .

Have you ever guddled for trout? Can you remember the excitement of it as you belly-flopped at a likely spot and plunged your arms into the water and under the bank beneath you? Your sleeves got wet but what the heck — they would dry later on.

You were too eager to begin with and the trout raced away the moment your fingers touched it. But gradually, you got the feel for the job and your gently moving fingers identified the part of the trout you were touching. Too near the head and the fish backed off, too near the tail and it swam forward. But touch it just on the belly and you had all the time in the world.

Ever so gently, you literally tickled its belly until you got your fingers exactly right. Suddenly, the trout flopped over into the cup of your hand. You didn't quite grab it, but your grip quickly tightened. Then, almost in one movement, whoosh! — you threw the trout from the water clear on to the bank. What did a wet sleeve matter then? You felt like a king.

I was reminded of trout guddling the other day when I was drafting fat sheep ready for the market. Every week since the new year we have been drafting some of the 600 fatteners in the hope that 30 or so might be ready for selling. "Will this one do? Is that one fat enough? Och, we'll take this one and let the grader decide."

This past winter has been much wetter than the previous three. As a result, the sheep have not fared so well — despite the fact that we started trough feeding them a fortnight earlier than usual. When the fields are wet, a sheep has not one mouth but five. The four hooves inflict as much damage to the pasture as the animal's mouth does. Ultimately, the field gets fouled by poaching and the grass does not last as long as in a dry season.

Well anyway, the weather has been warming up fairly early this season and the grass is growing. We are now finding that the combination of young grass is working wonders. Thankfully, the hoggs (as they are called after New Year's Day) are fattening quickly. When we tried them the other day, it was just like guddling. The hoggs were almost falling into our hands. They were just right.

To judge the degree of fatness or finish, you feel with fingers and thumb first the hogg's backbone, then the small of the back, then her hurdies. Finally, a firm grip of the tail will tell you if the animal is ready. One English buyer at Inverness market makes his assessment by turning up a few sheep in every consignment to feel their breastbones.

Sadly, there has been a great dearth of English farmers in the market looking for sheep this spring. The drought in England last summer was so bad that vast acres of pasture were severely burned. Their grass fields have apparently not yet recovered and it is doubtful if they ever will, unless reseeded. Similarly, the turnip crop failed for lack of moisture. This sorry state of affairs has left the English farmers with no winter keep for finishing lambs as they normally do.

There is one particular English buyer who is specially welcome because he can always be relied on to cheer up the trade if he is on the lookout for sheep. Needless to say, his name is Armstrong — the surname of a family that has been famous, or maybe infamous, as sheep and cattle raiders and traders for hundreds of years. Domiciled on both sides of the border, they regarded the wide, rolling territory as Armstrong country; and they swore allegience to neither Scots nor English kings.

In the history of the Borders, tales abound of Armstrongs being hung for reiving century after century. Fortunately, some have survived.!

Even today, the trading activities of that family and of others like them make a complete nonsense of any suggestion that an economic border should exist between Scotland and England. Our trade is too inter-dependent to be unravelled. For example, the trade for sheep at Cornhill and Thainstone is totally ruled by the prices going that day at Longtown, near Carlisle. From both these local marts, dealers phone through information regarding the number of sheep forward, the overall quality and so forth. And details of market demand are duly phoned back north from Longtown.

Now, lately I've been getting the feeling that a Scottish Parliament is somehow going to flop into our hands — and that quite soon. Will there be sufficient able businessmen and shrewd traders willing to man its benches? To make it a lasting success they will need all the wile and finesse of the expert trout guddler.

Progress is set to make its mark

I couldn't stand my granny and she had no great love for me. Anyway, it was purgatory for a restless little lad to have to sit quietly in the parlour listening to adults when there was a marvellous horse outside. Trigger was no more precious to Roy Rogers than Donald was to me.

Donald was my granny's horse and for years he pulled her gig to kirk and to market. He was jet-black with a white diamond on his forehead, three white feet and one black. At least, he had originally been jet-black. By the time I knew him, his face and tail were turning grey with age.

He let me clamber on his back while he was still lying down and, as soon as I had a firm hold of his mane, he would rise with a most peculiar see-saw movement. This experience stood me in good stead a couple of times in life when mounting camels in Egypt and Israel.

There were other, more beautiful, horses and colts on granny's farm, but Donald was special because he was a war horse. He had served in France, as an officer's mount in World War I, having been requisitioned from the farm in 1914 and bought back in 1919 after much wrangling with Army authorities.

If I pushed his mane aside, the six numbers branded on his neck were strikingly evident. The sight of that deep brand on otherwise-perfect skin always sent a shiver down my spine.

Even today. I hate to see the cattle brander, who calls at our farm twice yearly to apply his branding iron to the hip of a heifer.

When I kept 60 Ayrshire cows, their colour marking was sufficiently distinctive to allow easy recognition of each one. And besides, they all stood in byre stalls with their numbers marked on slates above their heads.

Later, when I converted the commercial Ayrshire herd to pedigree by a process of grading-up over three generations, the Ayrshire Cattle Society insisted that all calves be tattooed in the right ear with an indelible ink.

This was done by a forceps with spiked numbers squeezed through the gristle of the ear. Although the operation was generally bloodless, I hated the job.

In the early 70s, I switched breeds from Ayrshire to Friesian purely because of the superior beefing qualities of the Friesian offspring. Their black-and-white markings are much less distinctive, especially if the animal is mostly black and has no face marking. By that time, also, the number of cows being milked had crept up to 140, making identification increasingly difficult.

A further complication nowadays is the practice of milking the herd through a herring-bone parlour, where the cows stand angle-on to the cattleman. It is impossible to see their heads, since they usually stand eating from individual feed troughs.

Each Friesian calf has a small metal tag with a number inserted in its ear shortly after birth. Often, a larger plastic tag with the heifer's number in the herd is added to the centre of the ear just before she joins the herd as a mature animal at around three years old.

These tags are easy to read when the animal is facing you in the field or the cubicle house. But in the milking parlour, with only the rear end of the animal visible, a freeze-branded number becomes inevitable

Before he visits the farm, the freeze brander collects each day a supply of liquid nitrogen which he keeps well covered and insulated. He selects the heavy metal numerals required for the cow and immerses them for a few minutes in the liquid nitrogen. Then he presses them very firmly on to the hip for about two minutes.

The animals feel no pain, as the skin is completely frozen. A scar appears over the number after two weeks and, by the end of the sixth week, hair that was once black is replaced by white hair depicting the branded numerals. This number remains clearly visible for the rest of the animal's life.

I suspect that the method used to brand old Donald with his six figures in 1914 would not have been so painless. Most probably, red-hot irons, such as ranchers use on their cattle, would have been employed by the Army. However, it was another military regime where tattooing gave me the most horrific shock of my life.

In the early 70s I had the good fortune to be a delegate to the International Dairy Federation held in Russia. One morning, I joined in a post-Congress tour of a creamery in the Ukranian capital of Kiev.

It was customary on such visits to be greeted initially by the manager, who was a member of the Communist Party, then by the depute manager, who was a trade union leader, and finally by the person who was actually in charge of the factory — often a woman.

My fellow delegates and I duly arrived; but just as we were about to shake hands, the No. 1 in the line-up suddenly became ill and began to shake. He excused himself immediately and took no further part in showing us round the creamery — a tour which lasted some two hours.

Later, however, he joined us for a drinks reception and buffet lunch which the factory had kindly laid on. After a few vodkas and many toasts to peace between our nations, the manager explained to our interpreter why he had become ill.

In 1942 he had been captured by the Germans and had spent three years in the death camp at Dachau. The sight of our Western European faces so reminded him of the SS Guards and of the terrible atrocities which he had endured, that he was quite overcome and rendered totally speechless. It took him almost the entire duration of our visit to recover.

While the interpreter was telling us his story, the manager pushed up his jacket sleeve, unbuttoned the cuff of his shirt and slowly rolled up the sleeve. There, in stark blue dye, were the six numerals, each nearly an inch high, that the German captors had tatooed on his forearm.

The shock and horror on the faces of my companions easily matched what we had seen on the face of our host two hours before. Now it was our turn to be struck dumb.

But a new era awaits us. This is the age of electonics. The talk is now of identifying animals by implanting a small transponder in the base of the ear. This transponder will be read electronically to identify each individual animal and the information will be passed to a computer.

The mind boggles. Will I know at all times, courtesy of the computer, whether the sheep's in the meadow or the cow's in the corn? And will the computer scream a warning every time strollers leave a gate open?

The world of animal management and animal identification has come a long way since the days of Little Boy Blue or the Cow with the Crumpled Horn. Can we say the same about man's inhumanity to man and about his attitude to his fellow-creatures in the animal world?

So fare ye well, Drumdelgie

"There's a forest oot in Cairnie
that stretches far and wide,
It is the wood of Drumdelgie
on bonnie Deveronside".

There has always been controversy over the first verse of the bothy ballad "Drumdelgie" and there are several known versions. My version is, at least, up-to-date — even futuristic.

As it happens, the arguments will all be consigned to the bin of history in the next few years when the lands of Drumdelgie and its neighbouring farm, Smallburn, are planted with trees.

Today's arguments, between the new owners and the local planners, centre on the proportion of land that should be planted with conifers and the proportion which ought to go under deciduous varieties.

Surely the real and urgent controversy should be over the fact that such good arable land is being planted at all.

I have always been pro-forest. To my mind, Britain's poor showing as a timber producer is nothing short of a national disgrace. We still produce only a small percentage of our softwood requirements and a negligible amount of hardwoods. Clearly, an excellent case can be made for rapid expansion of the acreage under trees. However, in our own neck of the woods there are large acres of scrubland and poor moorland that could and should be planted before we sterilise agricultural land like Drumdelgie.

Throughout the 18th and early 19th Centuries, Drumdelgie was a typical North-east 'fermtoun', comprising a whole community of small farms and even smaller crofts. Crofters' families boosted their meagre incomes by providing essential services — as miller, blacksmith, soutar, joiner and so on.

The land itself was owned by the Duke of Richmond and Gordon and held under a complex system of tenancy and subletting.

This established pattern was to change dramatically, however, when as rapidly increasing demand for beef stimulated the larger tenant farmers to shift into production of fat cattle. North-east lairds welcomed this move as a means of securing bigger rents, and they actively encouraged their capitalist tenants through financial loans.

The Duke of Richmond and Gordon was in the forefront of this agricultural transformation and, in the early 1840's, he carried out a large-scale reorganisation of his vast estates.

Drumdelgie emerged as the largest farm in Strathbogie. Over the next decade or so the tenant brought in 445 acres from surrounding scrubland. Records show that 1500 cartloads of drain tiles were used to dry out the land. The whole venture was financed jointly by the capitalist farmer and the laird — the Duke charging his tenant interest of 5% on the loan.

Even in modern time, there has always been a certain aura about the farm derived, I would suspect, from its sheer size.

Drumdelgie and its immediate neighbour, Bogmoon, have been worked together for as long as I can remember, and stretch to nearly 900 acres.

Verse eight of the bothy ballad records that there was a time when the largest farm in Cairnie was worked by both horse and ox. When I first started delivering milk to Drumdelgie farmhouse and farm cottages in the 1960s there were six tractormen and four other workers. The farmer supplied them all with milk as part of their perquisites.

I twice folded Cheviot sheep upon excellent crops of swedes on the farm of Smallburn, and have good reason to remember the first year, because my appendix burst while I was stretching the wire netting. By the time I returned from hospital, three weeks later, the lambs were nearly all fat and were quickly sold.

Drumdelgie has had many owners in the past 30 years, most of whom have been non-resident. The size of the unit seemed to make it attractive to successful farmers from elsewhere who used it as a challenge to their managerial skills — with varying degrees of success, I might add.

Intensive units for pigs, calf rearing and cattle fattening were all introduced and often later abandoned. Usually these ventures were just on too big a scale and invited trouble from disease, inferior stockmanship and so forth.

I recall that, some years back, a new owner with more enthusiasm than commonsense smothered the entire farm with sheep. He expected the sheep-carrying capacity of Drumdelgie to be the same as the Romney Marsh in Kent. Now, the snow lies late in Cairnie around the 800 feet contour, and this particular farmer did not match animal numbers to available food supply. Small wonder, then, that his most frequent visitor in springtime was the knacker's lorry calling to collect sheep carcases.

The trials and tribulations experienced by that owner bring to mind a very perceptive comment I once heard at a farm sale: Davie, the farmer, was retiring after many years of working land that was wet, with a mixture of shifting clay and peat moss. I was discussing the incoming tenant with other farmers. "Both the new owner and the new manager have agricultural degrees so they should be all right", suggested one man. A second farmer shook his head knowingly. "Davie had the best degree for this place. He kent it," he said.

Drumdelgie is a farm like that: ye need tae ken it. Perhaps it would have prospered better had it been split into two units. However, the overall shape of the farm was such that it would have been difficult to carry out a division which gave each unit a reasonable share of the south-facing slopes and north-facing slopes.

The 1948 Agriculture Act gave a lot of Exchequer assistance to farms like Drumdelgie; the successive owners took advantage of improvement grants for the land and the buildings.

It is hard to avoid the conclusion that many simply got carried away.

Large sums of money must have been spent erecting the five huge silos that straddle the skyline west of Huntly and which are clearly visible from the A96 road. Because they are a prominent, unique feature of the landscape, they have long been used as targets for military aircraft on low-level exercises from throughout Britain. I know of no other farm in Scotland with five such structures in a row.

These tower silos were all the rage in the 1960s and early 70s. I am really glad I resisted the temptation to erect a silo tower for making grass silage. The filling of the tower is simple enough. With a cyclone driven by a tractor, the grass is simply blown up a pipe on the outside of the structure. That process held no terrors.

It was the unloading of the silos from the bottom with a rotating auger that worried me.

The best of farm machinery has a tendency to break down after a few seasons' work, and it invariably chooses Saturday afternoon or Sunday to snap — just when the local mechanics are many miles away.

The prospect of having to retrieve the broken parts from under 200 tons of silage towering above me did not appeal. So I stuck to making silage in concrete walled pits or bunkers. The capital costs were less, the machinery required for both filling and emptying was simpler, and the skills and technology needed by the farmer and his staff were less taxing. One good industrial loader did both jobs and many other tasks around the farm.

Now, I suppose all the expensive towers and their equipment at Drumdelgie will be redundant because no forester is likely to find a use for them. The input of public and private monies — recent and not so recent — will all go to waste as the tree roots find their way down to the water supply and choke or displace the drain tiles. If in a later century the land is needed for food production again, the cost of removing the tree roots will be astronomical.

The wet hillsides of Western Scotland, such as the Morar peninsula, should surely be afforested before good stock-rearing and arable land like Drumdelgie is lost. There is a crying need for a strategic national plan which would take all factors into consideration in deciding ultimate land-use.

Many of the hillsides of the West are virtually useless for stock because of the bracken which grows there year after year. No animals can graze the weed without suffering lethal bracken poisoning. It is strange that modern science has failed to find an answer to bracken menace. I dare say that with the easing of pressure to produce food at any cost, the pressure to find methods of eradicating bracken has also slackened.

Timber is now the growth crop. I wish my forester friends good luck as they try to produce more home-grown material. Anything they can achieve will help to reduce the drain on the balance of payments. Nothing is forever: there are always changes — some welcome, some not so welcome.

So perhaps we can look forward some day to a new song about Drumdelgie. Since Scotland is reputed to have a poet in every parish and a song round every corner, we may not have too long to wait for a new ballad. In the meantime, I'll borrow from 1707: "There's an end to an auld song"!

Will you come into my parlour

All I bought on my day out at the Highland Show was a new suit — a parlour suit because my old one leaks. The trousers and blouse are of the finest green oilskin to match my green wellies. I shall enjoy wearing it on my weekend relief duty at the milking parlour because it will save me from the soakings I have suffered recently.

What I really need is a new parlour! Don't ask me why the milking shed is called a parlour. It is actually more like a sweetie shop with its two-sided array of big jars. The new parlours I saw at the Highland are much more efficient than any that have gone before.

This was only my third visit to Ingliston and I expected to see more innovation at the machinery and equipment stands. It must be 10 years since I last attended the show and, apart from a significant increase in the size of tractors and bogies, there was not a great deal that had changed. Had I stayed longer and looked deeper into all the rows of trade exhibits. I might have found more to take my attention. But alas, for me as for many more of my fellow-Scots farmers, this is definitely not the year of the big spend.

Prolonged high interest rates have certainly curbed agricultural spending. But a similar recessionary trend has not been evident on Britian's High Streets, where credit sales and plastic money are playing havoc with the Government's money-control policy.

Make-do and mend has been the order of the day on farms for several years now. Worn-out machines have been replaced by purchases at farm roups — of which there are plenty.

More and more, contractors are being called in to perform tasks that require specialist machinery. Even if the operator's bill is hefty, at least there is no vicious overdraft to be covered in the 11 months of the year when the machines stand idle in a shed.

The great thing about milking machines is that they are in use twice or three times daily, every day of the year. So long as there is an electricity supply, the machines go on.

In more than 40 years, I cannot recall a day through winter and storm that we have been more than three hours late in getting the milking started. A stand-by generator which I kept in working order for 15 years was used twice, but on both occasions the Hydro Board power came back on before the milking was finished.

I really cannot speak highly enough of the Hydro Board and their most obliging linesmen, who have made such herculean efforts to keep the electricity supply available at milking times over so many years.

The new milking parlours have electronic milk-flow meters which record the cows' production on a computer in the office through the wall. They show up the yield just like a petrol pump at each cow point before the milk is released into the large-bore pipeline.

In my parlour, there are two rows of huge calibrated glass jars which show the milk being collected as the cows release it, but you have to peer round to read them.

I have never taken to the cold, clinical cavern of a place, although I have learned to dodge the tubes and milk clusters or teat cups as they fly through the air when the cow is dry. An automatic cluster-remover is activated by a float when the milk flow ceases and the clusters are pulled from the teats by a cord. All very effective, but really a bit Heath Robinson.

Many of the cows do not like them and speed up their removal with a hearty kick.

Maybe I do not favour the parlour system of milking because I had a very efficient milking method before. I used to milk cows in a byre that had a round-the-shed milking system. It contained only tubes and clusters, with no array of jars and other accoutrements.

Once the milker had switched on the milk pumps, he could shut the byre door and stay in the warmth. There was no need to leave the comfort until the job was finished an hour and a half later.

For several winters, I had the company of a tiny wren at every milking. The little creature would hop down the airline pipe and follow as I progressed down the length of the shed.

One man could milk five cows at a time compared with the 14 that can now be milked in a parlour.

Efficiency is ever the name of the game, but I don't have to like it. And most cows are just a number as they get milked and go through. Only those with something wrong are noticeable.

It is strange to enter a cowshed on the Continent, as I did recently, and see the farmers still using milking machine buckets and 10-gallon churns. Here, the introduction of pipe-lines and bulk milk tanks was a big step forward 20-odd years ago. They were introduced first in Scotland and four years later in England. Scotland has undoubtedly been the guinea pig for innovations other than the poll tax.

The milking I remember best of all took place in summer, 1946, in the days when some of our cows were milked by bucket machine and some by hand.

I had arrived home on leave one Saturday afternoon just before the paying guests came for their fortnight on the farm. Incidentally, there is nothing new in farmers sharing their homes with holidaymakers. It was an integral part of our economy in the '30s and '40s, and was most enjoyable as well as profitable.

Anyway, the daughter of this family, who had been coming for several years, was a lovely, sweet 19-year-old varsity student. She volunteered to help me with the evening milking — this third milking was restricted to the high-yielding cows. She claimed that she had learned to milk the previous summer when I had been away with the RAF in South Africa; and she was determined to show her proficiency.

The cows were tied in stalls and the two of us snuggled down on our milking stools between two fat, cosy cows and got started to our evening task. I don't recall if her milking technique had improved, but I can tell you that by the time the milking ended my kissing technique had improved out of all recognition!

She had the good sense not to marry me, though. She was bright enough to realise that, once you learn to milk cows, if you live on a farm you will get the job to do every day of your life.

Now, had I been a rose grower, I would have named a new rose variety after that lass. Well, I did the next best thing and named a sweet heifer after her. And now, more than 40 years later, I still have an Olivia family in the herd, looking well and milking well. But I assure you I have never tried to kiss any of them.

I know that courting goes on in parlours, but somehow I doubt if it takes place in milking parlours. In my parlour, you are more likely to get a kick than a kiss. Maybe the cows don't like my new suit . . .

Disappearing toonkeepers

I'm toonkeeper this weekend. I will be the only soul around the farm toon — chief cook and bottlewasher.

This year has seen our quickest silage-making ever, and although the pit will still need a lot of rolling before it is consolidated sufficiently to cover with polythene, the rush of the work is over. So my son and his staff are taking a well-earned respite after a busy springtime of non-stop work.

I haven't even a lot of calves to feed. The progeny of the huge Simmental bull we purchased last year are in great demand and they mostly find ready buyers at just over a week old. Contrary to our earlier fears the Simmental calves have so far presented no difficulties at birth. Maybe I'm tempting providence by mentioning the subject, and it will be just like the thing if the heifer expected to calve this weekend gives bother.

Before we bought the Simmental we had remained faithful to the Shorthorn breed for mating with heifers, but the calves did not meet such a ready demand as those from the Continental bullls. And I always believe in giving the customer what's wanted.

For several years now we have used a Limousin bull on our lower-yielding cows. This combination has produced great calves and they, too, have been much sought after. Just occasionally, some of our cows produce Charolais calves by means of AI. There are times, therefore, when we have calves of all three beef breeds — plus, of course, Friesian heifers reared as replacements for the dairy herd. This provides the opportunity to compare the behaviour of the different breeds.

Once you get them going, the Charolais calves are the most popular and pay best. However, they are often dorby when born and slow to get on their feet. Since we like to make certain that all calves get at least three pints of colostrum within the first four hours of birth, we often have to milk the cow and feed the calf with a bottle and teat. Even then we find that the dashed craiters will do anything rather than swallow. Patience can run very short. It is a well-known fact that women make a better job of calf-rearing than men do, although I am sure there are exceptions. I am not one of these exceptions.

Limousin calves are a totally different proposition. They are extremely lively at birth. Struggling to their feet within minutes, they will try to suck their mothers immediately. But for sheer ease of rearing there is nothing to compare with the Friesian calves. They seem to have been bred to drink out of a bucket — which they often do at three days old. I would put the Simmentals next in line for easy rearing.

Our native breeds of Aberdeen Angus, Shorthorn and even Hereford have greatly lost favour in the past 10 years. The Continentals have swept the board because of their quick growth and the fact that their evenly-fleshed carcases meet the preference of today's consumers.

I will try to get the calves fed early so that I can set off round the various grazings and check the cattle. It is unlikely, however, that I will be as fortunate as my son Michael was last Sunday. While going to the shore field at Portgordon before 8am, he saw a dog otter in the street by the sea wall. It seems the dog and bitch has been migrating to another burn and had become separated.

What with otters, badgers, foxes, mink roe deer, pheasants, partridges, peasieweeps and various other species, it seems that wildlife and intensive farming can co-exist better than the naturalist lobby would give us farmers credit for. As many of the animals are nocturnal, only the early riser gets the thrill of sighting them.

George Gershwin fairly got it right when he wrote the song about summertime, when the living is easy. Certainly, keeping toon in the summer is a very different story from the task in winter, when hundreds of animals are totally dependent on one man for their food at weekends.

I am well aware that nowadays many farms are run singlehanded by the farmer, resulting in his keeping toon every weekday and every weekend too. Where steadings give scope for adaption, a sizeable number of farms have developed easy feeding systems. But not everyone has had enough capital to carry out the necessary conversions.

The statistics from the parish of Kirkhill, near Inverness, would be typical of what has happened in most parishes of Scotland. On about 5,000 acres of arable land and grassland, there are now only 19 full-time farmers. In 1960, 75 men were employed on the farms. Today, there are only three.

Mr Charlie Gair, of Easter Moniack, gave me these figures recently, as well as kindly lending me some diaries of his father. From these meticulously-kept records of his farming activity I am gleaning lots of interesting facts about bygone years.

In the 1960s, Charlie and I played an active part in the work of the Scottish Milk Records Society and often travelled to meetings in Glasgow or Edinburgh. In those days, we were able to get away from our grindstones to become involved in running agricultural societies of various kinds. We could leave home with easy minds, knowing that our farm staff were as capable as we were. Today, there are few or no farm staff and it is becoming increasingly difficult to persuade farmers to take office.

It would appear that the process of labour reduction is irreversible. I don't forsee a recovery in the number of workers on our farms any more than I forsee a recovery in the British breeds of beef cattle.

I do not seek to sit in judgment on anybody, nor would I blame any particular body for the present situation. But I am prepared to state the bare facts. It's plain to see that workers have virtually disappeared from our farms. Somebody somewhere has priced good men on to the dole queue, while those who remain are grossly overworked. And the farmers will be the next to go, fed up with the worry and trauchle.

This past week, world leaders have congregated in Rio to discuss ways of halting the imminent disappearance of certain animal species from the earth. I'll bet not one word has been said about the disappearing toonkeepers. It will never hit the world's headlines, but the loss of their skills will greatly imperil the future economic and social fabric of Scotland.

In the meantime. the North-east still has at least one conscientious and (in the summer, onywey) willing toonkeepers left. So: I'll away and feed my "Continental calfies".

Parlour fun and games at milking time

August to October is the season for introducing new first-time heifers into the milking herd.

Everything could go smoothly if only there was some way of getting the animals to understand the rules of the game — especially Rule 1: we always win. It would be less costly in money terms and much less costly in time and temper if they would obey quietly and not try to do things their way.

With every dairy heifer at the calving currently costing £850 or thereby, there is very little room for mistakes. To get 10 settled milkers from 10 heifers is like crying for the moon. To get nine heifers with live calves and each one milking on four quarters is good going. Eight is average. Seven or less is disaster.

No matter how much attention is given by the person in charge of the calving field or the calving pens, one heifer will start to calve when no one is around. Perhaps the calf will get stuck, or some other complication will arise — and help will arrive too late to save the calf. What was worth £200 an hour earlier is now a carcase which must either be buried or given to the knackery.

Let us assume, however, that all goes well, with the calf on its feet and suckling. The four days' undivided attention bestowed by the mother gives it a good start in life. Unfortunately, this interlude also allows mother to become very attached to offspring, and when the time comes for separation, all hell is let loose.

Should you, by mischance, get between the heifer and her calf, she will toss her head — if you are lucky. If you are unlucky, she will toss you before you know what is happening. Obviously, it is disastrous to have a dog along during this operation because the very sight of one arouses the mother's protective instinct still further.

The easiest way to effect the separation is to drive both heifer and calf to the milking shed to join the rest of the herd. Once there, you grab the calf and while the mother's attenton is diverted, whisk it away and tie it in the calfpens so it cannot rejoin mother.

For the next 24 hours both animals will bawl incessantly. Woe betide the farmer and his family if their home is within earshot. The heifer, too, must be kept indoors and restrained for at least one day, otherwise she will make determined attempts to rejoin her calf. Fences are no deterrent at this stage and many a beast gets a teat torn by barbed wire if she is let loose too soon.

Quite the best cure for a torn teat or a punctured udder is a handful of cobwebs applied to the wound. The blood clotting properties of cobwebs are almost magical and I have never known a tear go septic after cobwebs have been used. I have good cause to be grateful to the dairy cattleman who gave me the tip more than 20 years ago.

We always keep the roof space of one wooden shed where the spiders are left undisturbed. Incidentally, the remedy works equally well on humans. Cuts and hacks in fingers can be cured by twirling a few strands of cobweb to about the thickness of a cotton thread and prising it deep into the hack. Keep it dry and the wound will close round the cobweb overnight. In a few days, healing will be complete.

But to return to the heifer, now devoid of calf. She has to be persuaded to go down one side of the herringbone parlour. If you are fortunate enough to squeeze her in between two big, quiet cows and to succeed in getting her nose into the feed trough, she may settle down nicely and obey Rule 2.

Rule 2 is: to keep all four feet on the ground. Alas, it is seldom obeyed. Usually, both hind feet are used for lashing out at anything that comes near, and both milker and milking machine are sent flying.

There is no point in striking back, as that will only lead to a fresh outburst of kicking. At this stage the kickbar becomes necessary. Every dairyman must be eternally grateful to the person who invented it.

The kickbar consists of three pieces of metal piping constructed in the form of the letter C, with rubber stoppers at both ends. By inserting one end into the animal's flank just above her udder and forcing the other end over her backbone, it restricts movement so that she can no longer kick out.

Rule 3: the heifer will have milk in all quarters. The milker applies the crucial test to the heifer, squeezing each of the teats in turn to ascertain whether there is a flow.

Sadly, that is not always the case. There may be a teat deformity from birth, making one of the teats blind. Again, she may have been a victim of summer mastitis, a fly-borne ailment that attacks both maiden heifers and cows in calf. The disease is particularly rife in early autumn.

Every effort is made to avert the problem by using fly-repellent eartags, by clarting the udder liberally with Stockholm tar and by spraying the legs and udders of the cattle with fly-spray and disinfectant. But, fortunate is the farmer who gets through a summer without a few casualties.

A heifer which is functioning on only three teats is virtually unsaleable and has lost at least a third of her potential value. However, most of us make the best of a bad job and milk the animal on three teats by using a plastic plug inserted in the fourth teatcup. Oddly enough, nature seems to compensate and the heifer produces almost as much milk on three teats as she would on four.

Provided there are no further mishaps to the other three teats, she can have a fully productive life in the herd. If, however, more than one quarter has been affected, the only solution is to send the animal to the pie trade, where she will fetch around a third of her real value.

Rule 4: the heifer will settle down within three days — otherwise I will lose my temper. The herringbone milking parlour, plus the kickbar, adds up to a much more effective system of taming heifers, than the old byre and stall method of housing cows.

I can remember some of the pantomimes we had with wild Irish heifers in pre-war days. Each milking was a kicking match and some never settled sufficiently to release their milk.

After the war, the very first Friesian heifer we ever bought broke Rule 2 completely. She was a big, bonny beast — about 11 cwt. in weight — and had given no signs of wickedness until my brother, Percy, sat down to hand-milk her in the calving box. She lashed out so suddenly that pail, Percy, the stool and all the ropes went flying in different directions. I rushed in to help and was horrified to see that, for a moment, all four feet were actually standing on his body, with the animal's entire weight pressing down on him. He escaped with bruises and they quickly healed.

Now, 40-odd years on, bruises take longer to heal. No one who works with livestock of any kind can avoid bruises sometime. But my friend the vet said before he retired: "I don't mind the odd bruise, but when my bruises get bruises — that really hurts."

There are some years when the heifer inductions go more smoothly than others. Here's hoping this will be one. There is also a wide variation in the docility of the daughters of some bulls. And I suppose it has been that way since man first domesticated the ox. Just think of the kicking which the first milkman or milkmaid must have endured! Thank goodness we had hardy ancestors — and Rule 1 applied even then. We must always win.

Sheep sales are a world of their own

Long years back, I unfailingly used to meet a well-liked crofter aquaintance somewhere in the vicinity of the sheep lines at Keith Show. "Aye well, Hamish," Tam would say, cocking his head under the Sunday bonnet, "here's the best rose of summer."

Old Tam's poetic pronouncements (usually word-perfect from Burns) were always spot on. With Turriff Show and Keith Show over, the weather may say it is still summer but the calendar announces autumn.

In particular, the calendars of sheep sales which daily drop through the letterbox prove beyond doubt that autumn has arrived. There is, however, an in-built calendar in every sheepman. For just as surely as birds migrate south in autumn, so, conversely, the sheepman heads north at this time of year.

Each farmer has his own favourite sheep sale where he likes to procure his wedder lambs for spring fattening. Or perhaps he prefers to buy ewe lambs and keep them a full year to sell as gimmers in October. Again, there is the farmer who aims to buy ewe lambs from the same farm or hill every year so that his flock all look alike.

Whatever, the buyer's preference, there are sheep in the Highlands to suit all purposes. Some buyers like to get their purchases home early, say in August. Others buy much later when the cattle are off the grass. Before crop-spraying became such an accurate and effective art, there used to be valuable stubble-grazing which suited small lambs straight off poor hill-grazing.

I have just cleared bales from a field of winter barley and the stubble is so clean there isn't enough food for a rabbit, let alone a sheep. But I have a close-grazed field of old natural grass that will suit some lambs, if I can buy them at the right price.

Throughout my farming life I have always found that fattening lambs leaves some measure of profit five years out of seven. That is a better average than I can achieve in any other livestock or cropping enterprise. In the two non-profit years, either the winter weather has been too severe or — worst of all — the lambs have been too expensive in the first place.

We can never tell what the market price will be in the spring; and the price can vary widely from week to week and from market to market. In an attempt to average out the income, and in the hope of catching some of the high weeks, I try to have the lambs with just the right amount of finish spread over a selling period of 10 weeks.

To get that kind of spread it is important to buy a varied flock with some fairly fat and some fairly lean. If the hill lambs have had a dry summer they should be in reasonably good condition.

Buyers from the North of England, from Fife, from Aberdeenshire and from Banff and Moray all compete for the hill lambs, The same faces can be seen at many of the sales year after year. Rumour abounds among buyers round the sale-ring. The North of England has had a prolonged

44

drought so the English farmers will not be buying at the early sales. The neeps in Fife are a complete failure . . . And so the congenial claik spreads from a' the airts.

If the dealers from England have orders to buy, they force up the prices. If they are buying on spec they tend to be much more cautious and keep a look-out for bargains. We buyers can purchase or not as the trade and the mood takes us.

It is the poor sellers I feel sorry for.

In most cases they must get rid of their flocks because the grass is becoming scarce on their thin pastures.

Moreover, in the remote areas such as in Forsinard, away up the Strath of Kildonan, there is only one local sale. To withdraw the lambs and present them elsewhere would involve a lot of expense and travel to either Thurso or Helmsdale.

Sale day in Forsinard can be heavenly or hellish, depending on the weather. There is no shelter for miles around and the site is boggy. A combination of wind and rain can produce a miserable day for all concerned.

At Helmsdale the market site is on the face of a steep brae, opposite and above the village. Heavy rain results in very slippery conditions underfoot, and the lambs do not look their best. But give me a fine day and there is no place on earth I'd rather be on a Saturday morning — with the Brora sale to follow in the afternoon.

Still farther north, at Dunbeath and Lybster, the buyer can choose between hill lambs and park lambs. The latter need better fodder than lambs straight off the hill grazings. However, they fatten faster and reach heavier weights than do hill sheep.

Wick and Thurso tempt the sheepmen with the real North Country Cheviot lambs. They are often too strong to suit my purpose and too expensive to suit my purse. Still, for those who seek ewe lambs of quality, these two places must surely be their Mecca.

The great first-day sale at Lairg has a special drawing power. More than 30,000 ewe and wedder lambs are sold on a Wednesday. One of my great regrets in life is that I did not go to Lairg as a young man to see the vast flocks of lambs being herded into Lairg on a sale morning. To one who likes sheep as much as I do, it would have been a wonderful sight.

Shepherds and drovers must clearly have possessed very special skills in successfully keeping these huge flocks separate.

All the sales I have mentioned are concerned almost exclusively with the throughput of Cheviot lambs. For buyers seeking Suffolk crosses, Blackfaces, Greyfaces, Mules or Continentals the more southerly sale of Dingwall and Inverness must be their destination. Inverness and Dingwall attract sellers from the West Coast and the Western Isles as well as from the Black Isle and Strathspey.

For many buyers, a week at the sheep sales is the only holiday they have and the only holiday they want. Over the years they will have made friends with the local people and can look forward to an evening together, and guess what they discuss?

Farm beasts beyond price —
Duchess, the cow; Peg, the mare

I have had to say farewell to the finest cow I ever bred or owned, Isla Duchess 12th.

She would not have taken any prizes at a show, even although she was a good looker. Show judges prefer cows taller than she was. Duchess, however, had something more than any other cow I have known. She had determination, or smeddum — or call it just plain guts.

Invariably, she was first through the gate on the way to the milking parlour, and she always found a place among the first seven waiting in herringbone formation to be milked. She stood there and bawled until the feed dispenser at her trough disgorged her cattle cake.

Because of a hopeless milk-quota allocation, we do not try for high yields. But for six months of every year, Duchess's ration was the maximum 8lb. of cake because she milked at her peak nine gallons a day and kept it up longer than any of the other 140 cows in the herd.

Milking over, she was first to the trough for her feed of silage and draff.

Often, at the late evening inspection of the herd, she was the only one still eating when her companions were resting in their straw-bedded cubicles.

She was the first to the field in summer, and would box with her head any other cow that tried to get through the gate before her. Bossy — yes; but not a bully.

So, why did I have to see her off after only six lactations?

Sadly, she failed to go in calf, and, having become infertile, her milk yield dropped quickly.

Despite every endeavour by our vets and ourselves, she came a-bulling every three weeks. We tried artificial insemination for the first six times, then four different bulls, subsequently, but to no avail.

Cows are often difficult to settle in calf after having given birth to twins, and few stockmen welcome multiple births.

The last time Duchess calved, nearly two years ago, she produced twins — the scourge of every dairy farmer. She had a difficult calving and my son, Michael, needed lots of time and patience separating the calves which were being presented together, hind feet first. Both calves were alive, but damnation! — there was one of each sex.

In such cases, the bull calf will be perfectly normal although small but the female calf almost invariably proves to be barren — a "freemartin".

After the trauma of giving birth to the twins, Duchess struggled to her feet, staggered and struggled again to regain her balance. A lesser beast would have collapsed. Many cows, after a less difficult calving than she had, lie for three days before trying to rise.

She suckled her calves for four days, then returned to the milking herd.

Within two weeks she was producing six gallons daily, and at six weeks she peaked at nine gallons.

After milking one morning, I mentioned to Michael, that Duchess was, again, top cow. He replied: "If we could capture and bottle what that cow has got, the world would beat a path to our door."

Just once before had I come across an animal with such determination — a mare called Peg. She and I shared four winters and summers on milk delivery. Her temper was vile, and occasionally she would try to take a bite out of my shoulder as I passed. She enjoyed rude health and never needed a day off.

When the going got tough in wintertime, Peg was outstanding. Confident and surefooted on ice, she did not once fall between the shafts during my association with her. In the long, hard winter of 1947, Peg never failed to get me home. At times we were travelling on packed snow higher than the fence-posts.

One particular stormy day, snow had fallen steadily since early morning. We finished the delivery in impossible conditions in mid-afternoon — three hours later than usual. The light was already failing. Peg scraped a path with her front feet, pulled the lorry forward a few feet, and then started into the scraping again. We got to within 400yd. of the farm steading before drifting snow hid it from view.

At this point, the drifts were level with the floor of the lorry. I was becoming weak from fatigue brought on by cold, soaking clothes and hunger. I wasn't much help to her, but still the mare kept trying. She just would not give up.

Finally, she gave one extra big pull. The lorry was stuck fast, but the leather traces snapped and Peg stood free.

I grabbed hold of the ends of the traces and lay down in the snow. She pulled me the last 300yd., plunging and scraping to reach her stable. It took four men and four Clydesdales to recover the lorry.

While I was in Parliament in the 1970s, I used to come into contact with a woman M.P. who possessed the same kind of determination as Duchess and Peg. Her name? I think you know it.

On the trail of McGinty's pig

Did you see the advert for the sale of the farm of Balmannocks?

Admittedly, it is now part of a much larger unit but there it was — and I have to eat humble pie. My apologies are due to the farm owners and to the good folk of the parish of Torphins because I earnestly believed that Balmannocks was simply the name of a fictitious farm that ryhmed with "dainty stammacks" in the bothy ballad about "McGinty's Meal and Ale" where the pig went on the spree.

As I dealt at some length with Drumdelgie a few months ago, it seems only fair to give some thought to the goings-on at Balmannocks the night the pig broke loose. "McGinty's Meal and Ale" is perhaps the liveliest of our North-east bothy ballads, and certainly the best tongue-twister of them all.

At the end of the harvest and before the temporary harvest hands dispersed to their homes, the farmer of Balmannocks invited them and his regular workers, their families and sweethearts, to a meal and ale — or harvest home. These events took place in the farm kitchen where space was very limited, and only near neighbours would have received a bidding.

While harvest homes were fairly common throughout the North-east faming community, it appears that the term "meal and ale" was prevalent only in Aberdeenshire. All my efforts at researching the history and nature of these particular farming revelries drew a complete blank in Banffshire and Moray. I could find not one elderly farmer or farm worker who had been present at such an affair.

Imagine my delight, then , when at Thainstone mart I ran to earth Mr Donald Henderson, ex-Provost of Kintore and one-time farmer and horse trader.

Donald could clearly remember attending a meal and ale at two different farms in successive years.

When he was a young lad in the 1920s, new village halls were springing up throughout the area. Intense rivalries arose between neighbouring parish committees as each desperately strove to raise sufficient capital to ensure that a hall would be built in their village first.

Offering space for a large number of dancers, and thus widening the scope for choosing a partner, these halls had obvious advantages over the makeshift facilities on the farms. They quickly became a magnet for young people.

Many organisations — football clubs, badminton clubs and so forth — supported the hall by holding dances regularly. Inevitably, the purely localised meal and ale ceased to be an attraction and soon became a thing of the past. Mr Henderson claims, however, that no village dance he attended ever captured the couthiness of a meal and ale.

While regretting their demise, he nevertheless does concede that they had one big snag: "A'body kent fa wis coortin fa" — and that was mighty inhibiting!

The "meal" part of the evening was something of a feast and certainly a great deal more than just oatmeal. The womenfolk of the house put a massive effort into providing a table heavily laden with all kinds of trifles, jellies and cakes. Invited neighbours also brought their contributions in carefully packed baskets. The fancy food was a rare treat for people who existed for most of the year on very plain fare — milk, meal and tatties.

While the farmer might have had a bottle of whisky for a few of his cronies, the ale referred to in bothy ballad was most likely to be fourpenny ale brewed locally and sold in five-gallon barrels. Mr Henderson recalls two breweries in Inverurie and one in Oldmeldrum, but he says he didn't like the stuff. It was too bitter for his taste.

Anyway, McGinty's pig seemed to like the ale.

The song tells us that it wandered into the pantry, found the toddy and "took kindly to the stuff like ony human body".

Although you occasionally hear tales of a dog being given a saucer of beer by its master, as a general rule animals do not like alcohol and have a very low tolerance to its effects. I remember once feeding fermented barley to hens rather than waste it. It made them squiffy almost at once and they became very unsteady on their feet. I cannot say if egg quality was affected, but they went off the lay for more than a week while they recovered.

My father kept a large square bottle of Johnnie Walker Red Label in a cupboard behind the biscuit tins; but like Mr Henderson, I did not like the stuff. The whisky was used for only two purposes. If any of us kids had an upset tummy, a saucer of sugar was impregnated with whisky, heated by a red-hot poker and set alight. After it had burned and partially cooled, it was supped — with many a shudder. It was usually very effective in inducing sleep and a quick cure by morning.

The second purpose was for dosing sick cows. Half a bottle of whisky mixed with two bottles of very strong, very sweet tea was poured down the cow's throat. The dosage would usually stimulate the animal sufficiently to encourage her to rise and hopefully to stay on her feet. Today, the vet can achieve the same end by giving the cow an injection at the base of the tail which will stimulate her very fiercely for about two minutes. The dose cannot be repeated.

I have no experience of the effect of alcohol on pigs, but I should think McGinty had one very sick pig on his hands next morning.

The music at the meal and ale was always provided from the company. There was never any shortage of people who could play the fiddle, the melodeon or the mouth organ, and there were often men who could diddle for the entire length of a dance. Some of the company would dance, sing or tell a story between dances, so the whole evening was really rather similar to the ceilidh in Gaeldom.

However, the meal and ale was held specifically to celebrate the end of harvest and not at the drop of a hat, as in the Highlands.

On the larger farms the traditional meal and ale was replaced by barn dances, which were usually held to raise funds for the local ploughing match association or the young farmers' club. My one and only attempt at running a barn dance almost ended in disaster.

The loft floor at Birkenburn was duly swept and the rafters cleared of cobwebs. A huge crowd appeared and dancing commenced. I was feeling reasonalbly pleased with myself when one of my staff called me downstairs. The floor was vibrating to such an extent that the ends of the floor beams were almost coming out of their wall supports.

I rushed back upstairs told the band to play only slow modern dances until half-a-dozen volunteers helped me prop up the floor with three rows of planks and rick poles, enough to take the bounce out of the floor. We told no one of the near disaster, but I was mightly relieved to see the dance finally end.

I know just how McGinty felt.

So: whether it be McGinty's meal and ale or Birkies barn dance, maybe we are safer in the village hall or the local disco.

Nightnmare set-asides scenes

I used to get nightmares — or rather, the same nightmare over and over again. And it was always self-inflicted.

My mother used to tell me I wasn't meant to be a gent, any time I wouldn't do some job or other. So working for a living has been my lot. Truly, I much prefer high tea to dinner, and a late meal is purgatory for me.

When I was at Westminster as an MP for five years in the 70s, I generally tried to snatch a half-hour between 5.30 and 6.30pm to visit the canteen. There, I might have fish, or macaroni and cheese, or some such dish, followed by tea and cakes. If pressure of Parliamentary business prevented this tea-time routine, then I would go to the first sitting of dinner at 7pm. Sure enough, most of the diners at that hour would be Scottish MPs. The second sitting was always more or less given over to the English. It was almost as if they were a different breed.

Some of my group colleagues preferred to eat late, and every now and then I would acknowledge with some remorse that I was being unsociable because I rarely joined them for a meal. So occasionally, after the vote was over at around 10.30pm, I would go along with them to some renowned city-centre restaurant — probably Greek, Persian, or Turkish. I invariably chose the lightest courses on the menu, but the meal would rarely finish before midnight and sure enough, I would have a restless night with a nightmare thrown in.

It was always the same bad dream. Back on the farm, I had missed out on one of the season's tasks. The fertiliser hadn't been put on the silage fields, or the turnip land hadn't been cultivated on time. There were umpteen variations on this recurring theme of minor catastrophe.

As the year went on, it proved impossible to catch up or make amends for my lapse, and things got steadily worse. October came and the silage still wasn't secured, or the neeps hadn't grown. With winter looming, there was insufficient food stored to bring the animals through the long months until spring.

The reality of the situation back on the farm was that I had excellent men who carried on perfectly well without me. But in the nightmare, utter chaos reigned.

As I travel around the countryside today and see the land that has been set aside under the EC scheme, I am reminded constantly of those nightmares. The set-aside scheme, where farmers get paid for keeping land out of production, has been running for two years and the fields are literally beginning to look like something out of a farmer's bad dream.

On the fields that were abandoned after a barley crop, the stubble of two years ago is filthy with weeds. In places, the land is baked hard like the western desert at El Alamein where nothing grows.

In the fields that were growing grass when abandoned, there has been rapid deterioration of the sward. The natural growth (that is, with no fertiliser applied) has been mowed each year but the dead grass lying on top has rotted out the finer grasses, such as the clovers and the meadow fescues. Rougher, stemmier grasses like cocksfoot and timothy are now predominant.

Entire fields have taken on a tufty, unkempt appearance; and the fact the no stock other than horses are allowed to graze there is complete anathema to me. If these fields were mine, I would have nightmares every night. It would be sheer hell at this time of year to have a field of grass that I could not use, while across the fence, my flock of wintering hoggs longed for a fresh bite.

Such a situation brings to mind the story of the Scotsman who was emigrating on the Canberra. Every evening at sunset he would appear in full Highland regalia and march up and down the deck playing the bagpipes with tears streaming down his cheeks.

On the night before their arrival in Sydney, one passenger could stand it no longer. He asked the piper: "If you love your native land so much, why are you leaving it?" The Scotsman burst out: "It's all this homosexuality business that's done it. A 100 years ago they would have been hung for it. Fifty years ago they would have been jailed for it. Now, it has been legalised. I'm getting out before it becomes compulsory."

If ever the setting aside of good agricultural land — land that I have tended and nursed throughout the years — becomes compulsory, I'll be emigrating. I like to sleep soundly at night.

Major's dam drowns rural optimism

On the farm of Birkenburn where I grew up, there were, as the name implies, birch trees and a burn.

Although the burn could be a raging torrent in winter, in summer it was an ideal place for children to play. Nowadays nursery and early primary school children are encouraged to play with water in the classroom as an educational aid. But me — I had the real thing, running freely outdoors.

At that stream many valuable lessons were learned that have stood me in good stead throughout my life. When damming the burn you quickly discover that a lot of water can be held back for a long time providing you let some escape. But try to dam it all and you get an explosion.

In Parliamentary Select Committees and in local council work I often carried the day and had my ideas adopted just because I was prepared to make concessions at the appropriate stage in the proceedings. The time always comes when you must let some water out.

One person badly in need of a basic lesson on making concessions is our present Chancellor of the Exchequer, Mr John Major. I wish I could give him some private tuition on timing of let up.

Everyone knows that Mr Major and his predecessor, Mr Nigel Lawson, forced up interest rates to try to halt inflation. Mr Major was trying to hold the water back and dammed the money supply by making it more expensive to borrow. However, he has held it too high for so long that he is now inflicting permanent damage on the infrastructure of our agriculture and, indeed, ruining many other industries.

I firmly support the economic argument that interest rates are a very clumsy weapon to employ in seeking his objective. In attempting to curb the consumer, he also hurts the producer of wealth or goods. He would have been better advised to introduce credit controls or even two tier interest rates to control inflation. To place an extra burden on farmers who are already hard pressed is crazy.

As I have pointed out before, Britain's farmers have achieved a quite phenomenal increase in productivity over the past 50 years. Had British industry as a whole done as well, we would be outstripping both Japanese and Germans in production per worker, and in Gross National Product.

Greater production and greater productivity do not come cheap, however, and most farmers had to invest heavily in buidings and machinery to step up output.

As recently as 1975, money could be borrowed at 8% — a level that was sustainable by farmers in all but the years of disastrous harvests.

In most years, too there was money available to repay some of the borrowings. With the current high rate, where money is costing 18% or more, repayments of the capital sum have proved impossible and, in some instances, interest is being added to the loan in an ever-spiralling tornado of debt.

Is Mr Major really so out of touch that he fails to appreciate that our farmers cannot absorb increased costs or increased credit charges? There is no way that farmers can pass on increased costs to the public. Processors and retailers can — and do — pass on their increased costs; so now we have a situation where the primary producer gets a smaller proportion of the shop price of food than ever before.

The constant stream of farm roups advertised in this newspaper bears witness to the numbers of farmers who are, week by week, giving up the unequal struggle. John Major has held his dam too long and has already caused permanent damage in the shape of rock-bottom morale.

And the longer he holds his base rate high the more dispirited will other farmers become.

Just as the trapped water undermined the foundations of my little dam, so prolonged high interest rates undermine the long-term stability of the entire British agricultural industry.

Restoration of confidence will now be a very expensive process. Only sustained periods of low interest rates will tempt the survivors to re-enter an expansionist phase. And let's make no mistake: expansion of our domestic agricultural capacity is essential to help to reduce the £5billion which this country spends each year on imported food.

We could well see a period when food production in Britain will rapidly fall — and the cost of importing to make up the shortfall will ruin the Chancellor's balance of payments.

However, if he were to reduce interest rates by at least 3% immediately, he might just stem the rush of farmers leaving the industry. There is only one word to describe his recent 1% cut — pathetic. It was the action of a man who does not have the courage of his convictions.

There is one further basic question I would like to ask Mr Major: Why hold the dam so tight? What is the point in maintaining the pound at such a high value? British industry and British agriculture could compete better in world markets if the pound were lower against other currencies. With an exchange rate of $1.9 to the pound I wish I could afford another trip to the US!

Although I studied economics and economic theory in my short wartime spell at St Andrews University and have retained a keen interest, I have always been even more interested in the laws of nature. And while I could write a treatise on my worries about Mr Major's mismanagement of our economy, I could demonstrate the points more clearly if only he would join me for an afternoon at that little burn where I played in my childhood.

Keeping rabbit population at bay

On Monday last I set 10 snares and at first light on Tuesday I went round my trapping lines. Imagine my surprise when I found I had caught six rabbits. One other had run, that is the loop had closed, showing that something had touched it.

This big catch demonstrates two facts: first, I have not lost my technique; and second, we have too many rabbits on the farm.

As it is important never to set snares in fields where sheep are grazing. I was restricted to a small field round a gully. I had noticed a proliferation of young rabbits there in the springtime, before the growing barley eventually hid them.

Many localities in Speyside and Inverness-shire suffered a serious rabbit plague this spring. I know one farmer who lost five acres of turnips because the entire crop was nibbled off before the plants became established. He had to sow a late crop of feeding rape to compensate.

However, during what must surely be one of the warmest summers on record, disease in the form of myxomytosis had once again spread through the rabbit population and greatly reduced their numbers — except in isolated pockets like my gully. It is vital that never again do we allow rabbits to re-establish themselves in the numbers that used to pertain in the 1930s and 40s, prior to the arrival of myxomytosis. In those days, despite constant snaring, rabbits could destroy 200yd, of crop adjacent to their burrows. Out of a 14-acre crop, the total destruction of four acres was a common occurrence on our farm. In addition, the stench of rabbit urine made grass unpalatable to all livestock.

At that time there was a ready market for rabbits, both to local butchers and to buyers in the South. One winter weekend around 1950, after a long spell of frost, 10 young farm lads went on an intensive rabbit hunt in Upper Banffshire using long loose nets strung along the fences. After three exhausting days they spent a crisp Monday morning loading four-and-a-half tons of rabbits at Dufftown Station. The receipt was duly kept for proof.

It would prove impossible to find an outlet for that size of catch nowadays. There is a very limited market for rabbit meat — although in one of Grampian's top restaurants I recently saw it on the menu at the same price as prime steak. I thoroughly enjoyed the dish; yet to my mind it was no match for the rabbit stews and roasts my mother prepared twice weekly when I was a growing lad.

As a rule, 16 were fed in our house each day, except Sundays. This necessitated a minimum of 12 rabbits a week; and so it was that rabbit catching became more of a job than a sport for us boys.

As well as snares, we had a wonderful collie dog which preferred killing rabbits to working with cattle or sheep. Bess never failed to catch the required number. The snared rabbits were saleable, but those caught by the dog were fit only for home consumption because they were marked on the ribs.

Bess's record catch for one evening's outing was 28, and I finished up putting a string round her neck so that she could help bring our haul home. I simply could not carry them all.

With a heavy catch like that you had to slit one of the rabbit's legs and thread the other leg through the slit, then carefully slide the carcase on to a long stick. In order to balance the load for the long walk home, the number of rabbits carried behind the shoulder had to be equal to the number carried in front. On that memorable expedition I had sticks on both shoulders.

One essential requisite for rabbiting was a good knife with a sharp point for gutting. Like many a hospital surgeon, we used to take pride in making as small and neat an incision as possible. The innards weighed approximately one-third of the carcase, so each animal was eviscerated as soon as it was caught.

To secure the best catch and to utilise the snares to full advantage the most effective plan was to set upwards of 100 and then get the dog to drive the rabbits from the crop towards the snares. Snared rabbits were quickly dispatched by a swift blow to the back of the neck delivered with the side of the hand — hence the expression "rabbit punch". The snare was then ready to be reset in anticipation of a second catch overnight.

It is said that in retrospect the days of one's youth were always warm and sunny. I don't remember them that way. Evening was the best time for rabbiting and on a wet evening the rabbits would be out feeding in force. Accordingly, my strongest recollections are of being permanently drookit; and oh, how I hated these short breeks chafing the backs of my knees!

Even as a youngster I could see the advantage of cross breeding. The hybrid vigour, extra size and better health of a crossbred rabbit was clearly evident. I would ask my school pals for any spare tame rabbits to set free for the purpose of interbreeding with the wild stock.

The black and white Dutch rabbit survived particularly well, although themselves on the small side. Much to be preferred was the occasional Blue Beveren, or an English Rex of any colour.

Quite the most successful outcross I ever achieved was from releasing a massive silver-grey buck which was too vicious for his young owner. The offspring grew to six or seven pounds, compared with the customary four pounds of the wild strain.

Sadly, the first generation cross of the silver-grey was too tame and easily caught, and very few survived into third and fourth generations. Those that did were beauties, being a lovely shade of blue-grey.

I never had the courage to buy a ferret and yet I enjoyed seeing them work in the burrows. In the hands of an expert, they could be very effective at clearing a difficult area such as a gorse-infected bank.

While ferrets look fierce, they are in fact usually very tame and loveable — unlike their close cousin the weasel which is a truly vicious killer.

Poachers, especially those with ferrets, were welcome, on our land. Contrary to popular belief these men were often keen naturalists with a profound knowledge of, and an interest in the local wildlife. I simply could not abide the estate gamekeeper who did everything in his power to thwart the tenants' legitimate attempts to hold the rabbit population down to a reasonable level.

But my long-running battle with the gamie is worthy of a telling on its own, sometime.

Humble barrow finds space

"Where is my barrow?" I asked casually the other day of my son and his two men as they were fixing a pulley to the muck spreader. My apparently simple question was met with blank looks.

"I've never seen a barrow about this place," said one of the lads, "and I've been here three years."

"When did you last have it?" asked my son. "I haven't seen it since we flitted here eight years ago. And what do you want if for now, anyway?"

"To barrow in some stones."

"Well, use the loader," said three voices in unison.

I could see the sense in their argument, but was reluctant to take their advice as I am no expert at handling tractors, especially in confined spaces. The front bucket of the loader is 7ft. wide and the door I have to negotiate is only 9ft. wide.

On this farm, we inherited a well-built shed with stone walls and slated roof which had once housed the threshing mill. The building had been of little use to us, however, because it has a 6ft. drop down to where the threshing mill once stood.

We decided to convert the place into calving pens, and we were fortunate enough to procure some of the strong wooden pens sold from the site of the Turrif mart. The timber rails and gates are in excellent condition, having been carefully creosoted annually. They will last indefinitely; but before we can get them erected, this muckle great hole must be filled in, consolidated and levelled.

Throughout the summer we have provided some free tipping space for local builders and civil contractors. To date, their contributions have half-filled the hole, but 20ft. remains open — hence my request for the barrow. It has not reappeared yet and we think it may be walled in behind a couple of hundred big straw bales. The fact that it has not been used for years brought home to me just how much the foreloader has revolutionised work on the farm.

Each and every farmer should give thanks for the life of Harry Ferguson because his invention of the hydraulic lift on tractors has put paid to heavy lifting. Foreloaders have improved greatly from the early, simple models of the 50s to the sophisticated power loaders that we see around today.

As well as loaders which can be attached and detached quickly from ordinary tractors, we now have specialist machines, such as Manitou, Sambron, JCB, Ford, Massey Ferguson and several others, which are not tractors per se but loaders only.

These machines have brought benefits to industries other than agriculture. For instance, few barrows are seen on building sites nowadays. Even wet cement is transported in the front bucket of a loader.

I can remember very vividly my first barrow. It was a present from Santa when I was five. Instead of doing his bulk-buying centrally, as that gentleman usually does, he ordered if from the local joiner who made and repaired our farm barrows. I would recognise his work anywhere.

Whether he had forgotten just how small a five-year-old boy is, or was allowing for my growth, I am not sure, but the barrow was far too big and heavy. I could barely stretch my arms to both shafts, and lifting it with even half a load of peats was almost impossible.

I cannot now remember if I went off Santa or the joiner first, but I reckoned that both of them had been in cahoots with my parents as two heaped loads of my barrow kept the house in peats for a day. Worse: the peat stack was at the farm steading a hundred yards away.

Needless to say, I formed a dislike of barrows at an early age — although I have done my share of barrowing neeps, silage and muck since. Wherever and whenever possible I have widened the doors of byres and sheds to allow access to tractors and trailers, thereby eliminating the double handling which barrow work necessarily entails.

The prime insult about my Christmas present was that it had a wooden wheel encircled by a heavy metal rim. And this at a time when the iron wheels on farm barrows were being rapidly replaced by rubber tyres. My barrow hit every stone and jarred my arms, whereas a pneumatic-tyred model just rode the bumps.

If we are proposing a toast to Harry Ferguson, let us raise an equally big one to James Dunlop who invented the pneumatic tyres.* There must be many men still farming who can remember tractors with iron wheels and who recall with little joy how awkward they were at practically every job, except ploughing.

These flat iron wheels were fitted with spade lugs to give traction and they certainly cut out wheelslip. However, the tractor could not be used for carting as the lugs dug deeply into the surface of the road.

Today, wheelslip has been virtually abolished by the incorporation of four-wheel drive on tractors. The use and adaptation of hydraulic power has come a long way in a relatively short time. Doubtless, there is scope for still further improvements. New uses will continue to be found for this most versatile of power systems; and I predict that on tomorrow's farms more than the barrow will become redundant.

So, if I can just have somebody to drive this expensive machine I will get these stones shifted. There are only four barrowloads to move . . . and my barrow and I could have finished them long ago.

Editor's note: Readers persuaded to adopt Mr Watt's suggestion should offer thanks also to the memory of Robert W. Thomson, of Stonehaven, who is claimed by the R. W. Thomson Memorial Fellowship to be the true inventor of the pneumatic tyre.

Tale of a savage encounter

On the farm this year, big bales are jam-packed into every suitable shed and a further 600 are stacked outside. The far end of the bale stack stretches from the farm steading down towards the banks of a burn that runs through a deep gully.

One day recently when everybody had gone to lunch (a meal I often miss), I took the tractor and foreloader to fetch a bale of wheat straw for bedding the calf pens. I am no expert at handling the machine, so I was driving cannily. Suddenly, in front of me, I saw what at first appeared to be a black cat fighting with something grey. As all our farm cats are grey, I thought that Blackie had returned from the wild to re-establish his supremacy.

This was no ordinary fight, however. Fur and skin were flying through the air and there was blood everywhere. I throttled back the tractor, eager to get a better view of the combat. It transpired that the savage encounter was a fight to the death between a huge rat and a big, black dog mink. The rat must have been very old to have attained such a size. Although it attacked ferociously and repeatedly, it was no match for the more agile mink.

This unusual spectacle was all the more surprising to me because we rarely see rats on the farm — apart, that is, from young dead ones which the cats occasionally drag home. The old lad must have been intent on making a winter home for himself among the bales.

A stack of wheat straw bales would provide warmth and shelter but no food; and it would be but a poor substitute for the corn stacks of yesteryear. In these rucks (for what self-respecting Banffshire farmer could persist in referring to "stacks"?), rats could spend a winter with an ample supply of oat sheaves for nourishment.

They had to run the gauntlet of farm cats and dogs perhaps once a day when, under cover of darkness, they ventured out to drink from a burn or mill lade.

Very few farm cornyards were totally free of vermin. Anything less than six rats per ruck was regarded as a light infestation. The farm dogs had a field day at threshing time and many of us kept a terrier specifically for ratting.

Prudent farmers took the trouble to ring the ruck being threshed with small-mesh wire netting to prevent any rats escaping and thus achieve a total kill. We used to leave the dead rats and mice lying and they were all gone by morning.

For once, the barn owls did not have to hunt for their supper. Indeed, the only creature to miss the abundance of rodents is the barn owl. Their numbers have dropped dramatically as nature balances the animal population to the available food supply.

The farm peat stack was another favourite place to overwinter and the terrier would never pass the peats without conducting a thorough inspection. With the demise of both the peat stack and the old-style cornyard, control of rats is much easier.

Today's grain stores, typically constructed of metal and concrete, provide no hiding place for vermin. Such improvements serve to remind us that hygiene standards of food production on British farms have never been higher than they are today. I doubt if we can say the same about imported food. This is one very good reason why we need still more home production.

Anyway, to return to my tale. The battle which I witnessed would undoubtedly have ended with the death of the rat had not my old collie dog come on the scene.

Both combatants scurried off to the banks of the burn, the mink to lick its few wounds, the rat almost certainly to die from its extensive injuries.

The mink was as fine a specimen as I have seen — and I have seen many since they first escaped from mink farms 30 years ago. His coat was longer than is usual and its sheen would have graced a stirk at a fatstock show. He would have made a lovely sporran if only I had been nearer with a stick in my hand.

Invariably found near water, mink have wreaked havoc on the wildfowl population. In this area, the only places to see a waterhen or coot nowadays are in city parks, such as Duthie Park or Hazlehead.

I keep on calling my little grand-daughter "a crazy coot", and yet I cannot show her what a coot looks like. One day I'll have to take her from the country to the city to see the wild birds.

There used to be a sizeable population of wild duck around the farm and it was most pleasant and amusing to watch the parent ducks leading a trail of newly-hatched ducklings up the burn. All the fluffy little bundles would be swimming for dear life, or stumbling and tumbling over the stones in the shallow parts.

The effluent from a dairy complex always contains some swollen grains which make ideal fodder for ducks and it was great to see small flights come winging in to feed each night just as dusk gave way to dark. But the spread of mink, the deadly killer, has changed all that. Young ducklings are very rarely sighted these days and even adult ducks are scarce.

As the mink is one of those species which kill for killings sake and destroy more than they eat, they have increasing difficulty in finding an adequate food supply by the banks of the streams. Consequently, they forage ever farther away from their preferred habitat of water and dry-stane dykes.

Now! Had I got to that fight before the dog, which animal would I have hit first? All mink are vicious killers, but rats are filthy, loathsome creatures. In my life-time I have survived three tractor accidents and two car crashes. Yet the only time I have known sheer terror was when a rat ran up the inside of my trousers. I haven't been the same man since!

It was high summer and I was wearing only light shoes, short socks and the wide-legged dungaree trousers which preceded today's drainpipe jeans. I was leading a cow by the halter when she dragged me into a dry ditch. The commotion scared the rat and it instantly shot up my leg.

Blind panic hit me when I realised what was happening.

Within seconds, it was behind my knee. Instantly dropping the rope, I grabbed at the rat with both hands and squeezed and screamed and squeezed ... I was convinced that I had been bitten umpteen times and had visions of catching one or other of the many rat-borne diseases — all of which are pretty horrible.

When I was certain that the creature had ceased to struggle, I spared one hand to remove my trousers. Out slipped one very dead, very squashed rat. And I had only been scratched.

Well, now you know why you will always find me wearing green wellies!

Sad case of homesick calf

I have just lost a calf, meaning in farming parlance, that it has died.

So what is unusual about that? It is a well-known fact that the only sure way to avoid losses among livestock is not to keep any.

I get losses like everybody else from disease such as scour, pneumonia and joint ill. These I can accept; but this particular calf died from homesickness and I could do nothing about it.

I like to buy cattle which have come off the Shetland boat because that island is virtually disease free. Moreover, the animals thrive when they get on to the lusher pastures of the Moray coast.

I readily acknowledege that parts of the Shetland mainland produce lush pasture during the short growing season. But beasts coming to North-east Scotland from any of Shetland's many islands will previously have been obliged to scavenge for fodder in a sparse, rocky environment.

I do not know where in Shetland this particular calf came from. Suffice to say that it was a nice Charolais cross heifer, probably some five months old and at a stage ready to progress to a diet of good hay, well-made silage and bruised oats with a protein supplement.

When it came off the float it was put in a pen with three other calves slightly smaller than itself, and was attended twice daily.

There was no automatic water bowl in that particular pen, and when water was poured into the trough it quickly became evident that the calf was not coming forward to drink.

I tried to persuade it with the bottle we use to feed newborn calves, but this calf just gagged and refused to swallow. We then isolated it in a single pen, close to the small calves, and offered small quantities of nice hay and fresh water so that we could monitor its intake.

Intake was nil. We tried putting salt on the back of the tongue to make it thirsty, but the calf managed to spit most of it out. We resumed force feeding with the bottle, but with no greater success.

Six days after its arrival, a very quiet old cow calved in the adjoining loosebox, so we put the ailing Shetlander to her and squeezed some streams of milk straight into the calf's mouth. The cow even licked the calf, but sadly its only response was to lie in the corner getting thinner by the day.

On the farm we use a stomach tube on young lambs if for any reason they fail to suckle their mother. We are reluctant to try it on calves, however, because it is so easy to put the end of the tube into the lungs instead of into the mouth of the stomach.

Nevertheless, taking great care, we persisted with this tube for three days, administering a mixture of milk and warm water three times each day. Never once did the calf show willing.

Then, 10 days after its arrival, it upped and died as the Irish say: When I saw it lying there streaked out I was angry, not just because it had died, but because it had died after getting so much attention.

I felt very much like the farmwife in a story I heard a long time ago. This old woman went to market to buy a cow. Eventually, she saw one that she fancied, and asked the seller, "Why are you selling the cow?"

"Just because I've got too many," the man replied.

"But why are you selling this one and not another one?" persisted the woman. "What is wrong with her?"

"There is nothing wrong with the cow, I assure you," the man said, and they finally did a deal.

The cow was duly taken home to the croft, tied in the byre, milked and fed. The woman went to bed somewhat easier in her mind.

When she entered the byre in the morning with her milking pail and stool, there was the cow streaked out in the stall, stone dead.

The woman became so mad that she went up to the beast, gave it a good kick and said: "Now I know why that man sold you, you old besom. You have likely done this before."

Homesickness is a phenomenon for which there is no pill or potion, but it can be a very real illness. With today's greater ease of travel and universal phone communications, the young person leaving home for the first time is not as isloated as formerly.

When I was young, many a student starting at university or college had to give up in the first term because of uncontrollable homesickness.

And the same applied to many a young lass with her heart set on a nursing career. The cure is immediate and miraculous when the victim returns home to familiar surroundings.

Back in the 60s, I used to sell good second-calf cows to a dairy farmer at Cruden Bay who pampered his animals much more than I did mine.

One December I sold him a young topper that I was reluctant to part with. As always, I had more heifers than stalls to house them so I was forced to take this prime cow to market, knowing that Mr Findlater would like her and give her a good home.

After four days he phoned to tell me that she refused to eat and was very dour. At seven days, he called again to say that although there was no improvement, the vet could find nothing wrong.

Absolutely certain that the cow would revive, I said I would accept full responsibility for her.

Cruden Bay was a long way off my normal route and it was next market day before I arrived at the farm with my slow cattlefloat.

So, 14 days after she had left me, I saw the good cow again. There she lay — unable to rise, emaciated and with horribly sunken eyes.

She had good food and fresh water in front of her, but would touch none of it. With great difficulty we got her on to a pallet and with the aid of a front loader, manoeuvred her into my float.

I really doubted if she would survive the three-hour trek home.

For the duration of the journey she lay flat-out looking decidedly uncomfortable, and in that position she remained as I lowered the ramp of the float.

I fetched a halter and hauled her into a sitting position whereby she faced out of the lorry. Well, miracle of miracles; she opened her eyes, recognised her surroundings, struggled to her knees and scrambled down the ramp to the ground.

Once there, she accepted a drink of water from a pail, then shook her lugs and let out a roar. A cow in the byre close by answered her.

Staggering to her feet she walked drunkenly to her accustomed stall and promptly started to box the heifer which had usurped her place.

The cow subsequently made a speedy recovery and came back to almost full milk production, although she took most of the year to regain her original bloom.

She was a grand cow to me for many years after that. A happy ending, but at that time it was a gie close call.

The drain brains

Little Bo Peep lost her sheep and maybe someone, somewhere once searched for a needle in a haystack. Me? I can't find our mill lade.

At one time there was a meal mill on our farm, as well as the threshing mill, so I expect there had been separate mill dams and separate mill lades. Every drop of water would have been precious, and somebody long ago drained a spring direct into the lade. When the mills become redundant and the lades were filled in, no outlet was provided for the water from this spring.

Throughout the last three dry winters there was no trace of the spring. Now, following the long spell of heavy rain in December, the water table has been restored and we have a leak that spills on to the road near the farm. During the recent frost, the warmer water from the drain has kept running, freezing only when it spreads over the road surface.

The resultant skating rink is not appreciated by man, beast or tractor. Mind you, I can't help laughing at the look on the dog's face as he slides all over the place. But it is not funny when the one falling is me. Somehow the dunts get harder as the years go by.

We have made several unsuccessful attempts to discover the path of this particular drain. Personally, I would prefer to find the source and cut a new channel for the water, thereby avoiding the need to dig up the road.

If the drain in question were part of a drainage scheme, it would be fairly easy to trace because throughout the North-east field drains are laid down to a common pattern. This takes the form of a herring bone or a half-herring bone, with each spur joining the leader drain at 22-yard intervals. Twenty-two yards was known as a chain; and this was the standard unit of measurement for drains, ditches, fences and so forth.

The other day I came across the chain my father used. A gey proud laddie was I when he entrusted me to hold one end of it while he measured the new drains or ditches that were due to be paid for.

With the universal adoption of the metre and hectare, all the old units of measurement — chains, roods, poles and perches — have sunk into oblivion. Today's school-children should thank their lucky stars for the introduction of decimalisation. My father had to grapple with arithmetical problems, such as how much to pay a drainer who had dug 136 chains, 12 yards at twenty-two shillings and six pence per chain. And he didn't have a calculator.

Although they would never admit it, many farmers secretly like plowtering in drains. A wee boy's pleasure at jumping in puddles dies hard. Nevertheless, the sides of opened drains are invariably wet and many a case of rheumatics in the hip has its origin in fixing a burst drain.

Prior to the invention of the rear-action hydraulic digger, spades were the sole tools used in draining. It was hard, excruciating work since the main drain or leader was 3ft deep and the laterals 30in down. If the ground was undulating, the depths were greater as the fall on the drain bottom had to be constant with no deeper spots which would allow the water to lie back.

Most drainage systems work faultlessly, but should a wet patch appear because of a collapsed drain tile or a choke caused by silting, investigations should start at the spot where on e drain joins the other.

One of my most enjoyable journeys took place in 1976 when I was a member of a small Parliamentary committee investigating the problems of the fishing industry. The cheapest way for the eight of us to get from London to Whalsey in Shetland was to charter a small plane from Biggin Hill in Kent. On a lovely May day we flew the entire length of England and Scotland hugging the East Coast at an altitude of 2,000ft.

From the height I could clearly see practically every drainage scheme that had been laid. Most farmers possess no maps of their drains, and I have often wished for a leisurely balloon flight over this farm to get a clearer picture of the location of the various drains.

I consider myself fortunate to have been farming during the expansionist days of the 50s when much boggy land was drained and limed with the help of Government subsidies. Farmers were encouraged to go for maximum food production from Britain's own resources, and dramatic improvements were made to the productivity of the land.

By 1952, most of the fields on our farm near Keith had been dried by comprehensive drainage schemes. The work was carried out mainly by squads of Irishmen under the direction of two men, both named Barr. What they didn't know about draining wasn't worth knowing.

Yet one of our hill foot fields defied us. Eventually, my brother, Percy, and I devised a major scheme which involved going down 8ft to the water-bearing gravel. The aim was to catch the water before it started to rise and soak the lower parts of the field.

Nowadays, gravel would be used for infill on top of the two 6in. drain tiles we were laying, but no such material was available then. Our solution was to use bunches of straw from the threshing mill packed twice as hard as normal. We hired a big RB shovel and driver from the local quarry and got going.

The draining was supposed to be a two-day, weekend job. All went well on Saturday. Frost had made the ground surface rock hard and the massive digger stayed on top. We started in about 5ft and garadually worked down to 8ft as we crossed the slope and hit the gravel level and the water. By the end of the day two-thirds of the length had been completed.

Then — disaster. A rapid thaw set in overnight and on Sunday morning we were sliding about in soft clay. Spooty clay, as it is known, started to flow in from the steep sides of the trench. Then about 40yd of one side caved in, taking with it the 10ft ladder we had been using to descend to drain-laying level. The heavy digger tried to move backwards and proceeded to sink. The upshot was that despite a hard day's work by four people, no track was dug on Sunday.

Next day we attempted to manoeuvre the tracked digger on to some old railway sleepers. On Tuesday we fetched more sleepers and a further 10yds were dug. That night, however, the rain came on and forgot to stop. The quagmire worsened; and after the drain was finally finished we had to lay a sleeper road two sleepers deep to get the digger off the field to hard-standing. It was slow work because we had only sufficient sleepers to lay twice the length of the machine at one time. On the 10th day it was clear.

The final infilling of the drain had to wait until high summer. Our trials and tribulations brought a lasting reward, though — nothing less than the transformation of a moving bog into highly-productive soil.

Incidentally, 40 years on we still haven't seen the ladder. I hope it does not take me as long to find the mill lade.

Down memory lane . . .

Perhaps the most rewarding aspect of contributing to this column is the wonderful feed-back I get from readers. Every article seems to jerk the chords of memory, with people recalling holidays on the farm and other interesting country incidents.

Particularly pleasing is the knowledge that so many non-farming folk apparently enjoy reading my ramblings and reminiscences.

I hope I do not give the impression that the days of long ago were somehow better than the present day — because they were not. When I was a lad, times on the farm were hard for master and servant. We worked all the hours that the Lord sent; and being caught with a book in your hand was a fault. So I hope I bring out the contrast fairly.

Winters were long and breeks were short. The stormy months stretched out interminably because the snow did not get cleared as it does today. There were no gritters patrolling the roads and pavements, scattering the mixture of sand and salt which encourages snow to melt whenever the temperature rises. Snowploughs pushed the snow to the side of the streets in heaps, then householders shuffled more of it from the pavements on to these same heaps. When the lot froze, it formed an almost impenetrable barrier for young milk-delivery boys. Getting from street to doorstep involved a feat of minor mountaineering for lads like myself.

I'll willingly pay poll tax or whatever to have the present standard of snow clearance maintained. This service costs Grampian Region £100,000 — yes, one hundred thousand pounds — for every snowy day. In the roads budget, allowance is made for a winter with 30 days' snow, bringing the total allocated to £3million. However, this sum is rarely required these days, suggesting that the winters must be getting shorter or less snowy.

As for those short breeks, they were an abomination. Boys wore them summer and winter. We were 14 or 15 before we graduated to "langers". On a wet day, the trouser ends got soaked and stayed soaked at the back of the knee. When it turned frosty at night, the wet trousers froze. Many a quiet greet I had from the sheer misery of it as I sat behind my father on the open horse-drawn milk float. The journey home took 20 minutes and on a cold, rainy or pitch black frosty night it was no joke. Thankfully, improved hygiene and more efficient refrigeration put an end to twice-daily milk delivery.

So don't anyone get the impression that I hanker after the old days. I am an enthusiast for change, as modern conveniences mean higher living standards for more people. For instance, I personally give thanks every day for the Hydro Board and the many luxuries brought to us by electricity.

Some things can go too far the other way, though. I would put the introduction of shell suits and jump suits for children's leisure wear into this category. In my youth we wore "Scudding claes" for scudding about — not, as now, expensive "playsuits for play". Clothes that were too old or tattered for school use were duly worn out in the rough and tumble of play at home.

Good times or hard times, the old times never fail to bring a touch of nostalgia. As I mentioned earlier, I have been delighted by the many fascinating responses to topics covered in some of my previous articles. I am greatly surprised, for example, at the number of people who recounted to me the horrific experience of a rat running up the leg.

Mr William Grant, of Little Ward, Huntly, was actually bitten by a rat that got stuck behind his knee. Although he gripped and squeezed the brute as I did, unfortunately he succeeded only in grasping its back end. He treated the bites with nothing more than iodine, and was indeed lucky to escape without infection.

Like me, Mr Grant now wears wellies everywhere on the farm. These wellies are in themselves a grand conversation opener. Often, folk who have never spoken to me before greet me with the query: "Far are yer green wellies, then?"

Barrows have also proved a topic of interest. One farmer told me his barrow invariably had a soft tyre when unpleasant jobs needed to be done. He learned how to blow the tyre up by using air in a tractor tyre, and he taught the technique to his men. But inflation of a different kind brought a sorrier tale from a friend I met at the mart. Lamenting the price of a barrow he bought recently, he felt that he should have got a tractor bogie for the money he was asked to part with.

I was very pleased to hear from a lady who remembered my homesick cow at Mr Findlater's farm. A close neighbour, she recalls Mr Findlater asking her to call at Tuechan Farm (the name had escaped me) to see the ailing heifer and suggest possible remedies. She never knew the cow's fate until she read about it in "Farm Journal" recently.

Many readers have passed on stories of homesick cattle, and of homesick cats and dogs that made their way back home. Apparently, horses are particularly prone to homesickness. Councillor Hamish Proctor, of Elgin, told me of one sad case from the early days of World War I.

Along with other young men from Moray, he was drafted to a cavalry school in England. One of the lads had strong empathy with horses and became closely attached to his mount. Sadly, while he was on the eight-week course his father died. He was given compassionate discharge to return to Elgin to run the farm, and his horse started to pine as soon as he left. The remaining troopers persistently offered it sugar lumps, carrots and other tempting morsels, but it steadfastly refused to eat and died within three weeks.

All these varied observations by readers have been of great interest to me. To date, however, there has been no response from John Major or his successor at the Treasury, Norman Lamont. The two reductions in bank interest rate of half a per cent each time will do nothing to stop the recession deepening.

I warned them that nothing less than a 3% reduction will turn the economy around, But maybe they don't read the "Farm Journal" of a Saturday.

Russians need lesson on food distribution

There are a lot of hungry animals in Russia and Eastern Europe today. Every stock-keeper there must be hoping for a warm spring and an early turn-out of cattle and sheep to the pastures. Many of the ruminants will survive, but millions of pigs and poultry will die for lack of grain and other essential feedstuffs.

Weatherwise, the harvest of 1990 was good but the chaos caused by perestroika and the subsequent lack of firm directives from the centre meant that fodder was left in the fields to rot instead of being stored safely for feeding the animals through the winter. The plain fact is that nobody knows whether they are coming or going.

When Stalin emerged as undisputed Soviet leader in December, 1925, his basic intention was to make the USSR economically independent of capitalist countries.

He energetically proceeded to put into effect his aim of "socialism in a united country". This objective involved total State control over the means of production, distribution and exchange.

Under his first Five-Year Plan, initiated in 1928, eight to 10 million of the more prosperous peasants (the kulaks) and their families were wiped out or deported as forced labour in the ruthless drive to make collective farming work.

Stalin issued orders to the collective farms from central offices.

Invariably, there were mistakes and disasters because of bureaucrataic control. Even when farmers met production targets the produce was often lost or wasted due to lack of proper storage or distribution. Worst of all, nobody very much cared.

The system could cope with basic production but it could not cope with surpluses. Equally, it was ill-designed to sustain a variety of products.

In lettuce week, everybody ate lettuce and in spring onion week everybody ate spring onions. But you couldn't get lettuce and spring onions at the same time.

Only someone who has been to Russia or its satellite countries — Hungary, Poland, Romania, Bulgaria, for example — can properly appreciate the desperate, widespread chaos resulting from agricultural collectivisation.

The EC may have its persistent (if relatively minor) problems caused by overproduction in some sectors, and politicians may bleat on about the disposal costs of the food surpluses.

Yet, anyone who has seen the empty shops and the long queues for food in Eastern Europe, then returned to confront the crammed shelves in our supermarkets, will tell you which system they prefer. Our consumers are almost spoiled for choice the whole year round.

I am genuinely sorry for Russia and its neighbours because most of them have now started to reverse the process of collectivisation and the centralisation of decision-taking. Unfortunately, they will find it very difficult to change from one system to another. Grave shortages of food are bound to occur during the transition period.

We farmers in Scotland really do not appreciate just how fortunate we are in having such an efficient distribution chain. There are the specialist firms such as Buchan Meat, Grampian Country Pork, Grampian Country Chicken, Aberdeen Meat Co., McIntosh Donald and several others — all specialists in their field. These firms often handle only one product, processing and distributing it to supermarkets or wholesalers.

We are equally indebted — and let us never forget it — to the men and women who stand at our auction marts and buy whatever the farmer cares to put on offer.

I have previously mentioned the invaluable service that Messrs Kelly of Larkhall have given us for 70 years. There are many others, though, who buy a wide variety of livestock and distribute to a diverse range of outlets. All of them are vital links in the food chain which goes from producer to consumer.

Fitting into this category are Ian and Edward Johnston of Fintry. Although they would not regard themselves as essential links in any agricultural chain, I reckon that without their efforts, a great many sheep and pig farmers would be ill-off.

Each market day they buy stock from every sector — fat pigs, sows and boars, prime lambs. old ewes and rams, prime cattle, old cows and bulls.

The animals are consigned to more than 20 outlets, different classes of stock going to the appropriate customers. The Johnstons have to get it right and meet the specific demands of each customer.

In March and April, they may buy as many as 1,000 fat ewes in a day. Just think of the multitude of grades in that lot. There are around 20 different breeds and crosses of sheep, and the animals on offer vary from the very fat to the very lean.

What suits the butcher's shop in Stornoway may not suit the Pakistani butcher in Bradford or the halal butcher in Birmingham. Some customers want the animals live, others want them in carcase form. Yet again, some are interested in buying only certain cuts. Handling this sort of trade must require sharp administration, but Ian Johnston tells me he has only one office employee.

Other North-east companies and individuals — for instance Ron and Ian Mathers of Kintore, Mrs Don of Old Rayne and Messrs Harries of Fountainbleau — faithfully seek to cater for various sectors of the market.

The task of these buyers is by no means straightforward. Although they will purchase whatever the farmer chooses to bring to market on a particular day, it may be several days — weeks even — before the customer is prepared to order the stock from them. Nothing less than whole farms have to be set aside to accommodate large numbers of beasts and keep them in good condition for indefinite periods.

These buyers in our midst have to anticipate demand and iron out the peaks and troughs of supply and demand. At that business, individuals will always beat companies.

Now then, Mr Gorbachev: where are you going to get the Ian Johnstons of this world to make your distribution system work? Their kind of expertise cannot be learned from a book. Your predecessor. Joseph Stalin, eliminated the entrepreneurs and the risktakers away back in the 30s.

You certainly have my sympathy in what you are trying to do — but I do not envy you your task. I'd rather be in my green wellies than in your shoes right now.

Lament as Highland board passes away

"Reform, reform. What's all this shouting for reform? Aren't things bad enough already.

These words are creditied to a learned judge of the last century. They came to my mind when I heard the highly-successful Highlands and Islands Development Board was to be replaced by Highland Enterprise.

This new organisation will comprise a whole series of enterprise boards throughout the Highlands and their remit will cover industrial training as well as the distribution of aid and advice to industry.

While I wish these enterprise boards every success in the future, I nevertheless doubt if they will adequately replace the HIDB. The board has done a lot of good work but it had still a great deal to accomplish. Sadly, many of the tasks which the HIDB would have tackled and the projects it would have advanced in the years to come do not fall naturally within the scope of the new organisation. But then I'm biased — and for two reasons.

In the late 1940s, the then Labour Government set up a commission to look into the problems of the Highlands and Islands. The man appointed to chair the inquiry was the late Sir Tom Taylor, principal of Aberdeen University. It was my great good fortune to know him well.

Like me, Sir Tom was a Keith loon and he always spent the Easter break in his home town. Every afternoon he would set out on a long walk and one of these excursions took him past a field where I was folding Cheviot sheep on turnips. He was a very sociable person and we got talking about the problems involved in reducing the many disadvantages which beset the Highlands and particularly the islands', livestock producer.

Tom Taylor had a brilliant, inquiring mind. He would ask for my thoughts about an integrated transport scheme and about the need for flat rate transport costs to get the livestock to mainland markets. A typical academic, he insisted I commit my ideas to paper so that he could use them in the inquiry.

I described to him the many deficiencies suffered by hill lambs and I explained that unless they received regular dosing with a copper and cobalt solution they would not thrive. He was particularly intrigued by the sheep with no ears. This deformity was brought about by a disease known as the yellows, which caused parts of the ear to turn yellow and rot away.

Tom Taylor formed the view that a great deal of work ought to be done by some body to identify and remedy the serious deficiencies that occur in the western seaboard and in the islands. He felt that if only the affected animals could be treated before they were taken to market then the Highland crofters' stock would lose their unenviable reputation as ill-thrivers. And, of course, it followed that the animals would command a better price.

Anyway, the Government accepted many of the Taylor Commission's recommendations. The HIDB subsequently thrived and it immensely improved the economic life of the Highlands. Regrettably, however, none of the board members or the officials addressed the problem of mineral deficiencies in the diet of the livestock. Crofters and shepherds were expected to use the standard mineral mixtures sold by feed companies, but what was really required were mixtures specifically tailored to the needs of each district. The deficiencies experienced in Lochinver were very different from those of Lewis, and the mixture which suited Tongue was ineffective in Tiree.

Much valuable work on the multi-faceted problem of mineral deficiency was done over the intervening years by well-respected Keith veterinary surgeon Stephen Cowie. In his capacity as the local meat inspector, Mr Cowie examined the carcases of red and fallow deer handled by North-east game dealers. So we can take it that the extent of the problem is known — but we are no nearer a solution than we were in the 40s.

In this winter of 1990/91, I have lost quite a few lambs through deficiencies of copper cobalt, selenium, vitamin B and God knows what else. These lambs came from an island west of the Hebrides. I've thrown everything but the kitchen sink at them to stop them pining and dying. It is small wonder that many mainland farmers prefer to breed their own lambs for fattening rather than be troubled with "ill-doers". And yet, the Highlands are the natural place for ewes and hill cows. Indeed, that is the only kind of stock the thin upland soils can support.

The heavy rainfall in the West leaches calcium from the soil at a faster rate than in the East. As a result, grazing livestock cannot get from the local herbage sufficient levels of this mineral to build strong bone structure in the early months of life. Without a doubt, the ending of the lime subsidy was ruinous for these remote Western areas. Built into it was a transport element which enabled the farmers and crofters to apply lime to their pastures at reasonable cost. At no time from its inception in 1936 until its demise in 1976 did the lime subsidy cost the Exchequer more than £6 million per year. Surely it was money well spent.

I maintain that throughout the years, the HIDB and the Department of Agriculture and Fisheries for Scotland (DAFS) did a good job of improving the breeding sheep and cattle in the Highlands and Islands through the premium ram and bull schemes. But unfortunately, they rather neglected the health status of the stock — a status that could have been greatly enhanced at very little cost. It is sad to realise that the pioneering work of Steve Cowie and others gets more recognition on the international veterinary scene than it does in its own country.

As things stand, the markets in the West are often short of buyers. Last autumn the trade for small lambs and ewes hit rock bottom at the late sales. And the proposed ending of the sheep premium will make things even worse this coming back end.

So, the HIDB is now no more — scrapped with a great deal of its potential for regional improvement unfulfilled. Sir Tom Taylor's dream nearly came true. Government ministers and spokesmen strongly claim they have not killed his creation. Well, maybe not. But they have most certainly castrated it

Farming downturn means smiddies are busy again

"Doing work for farmers is like working for a charity." a blacksmith I know told me the other day. "You just can't charge a decent rate for the job."

This hurt, coming so soon after a similar retort by a builder from whom I was buying material to rebuild a shed. "You'll be wanting it at farmers' prices, likely?" said he. "What's that?" I asked. "Somewhere less than half!" he laughed.

These remarks demonstrate how badly farmers' buying power has deteriorated. This unhappy situation is in turn, a reflection of the fact that the selling price of farm produce is too low. In reality, it is the farmer who is being charitable to his customer, the consumer.

Both blacksmith and builder are lucky to have had the distillery trade putting jam on their bread in recent years. Yet, as we have seen in the past, the whisky industry can go into recession, close down production and halt investment.

By contrast, if farming is in recession the blacksmith is increasingly in demand to postpone the day when implements and machinery must be replaced.

At present, our blacksmith's skills and ingenuity are being stretched as fully as they were during the 30s.

In those days the smith had to be truly versatile because he was called on to repair virtaully all implements. The agricultural engineer, replete with a multitude of spare parts, only came into his own in the 50s and 60s as farm machinery became more sophisticated.

I loved being sent to the smiddy with a pair of horses. Sadly, since our horses were usually placid I very seldom had the luxury of watching the smith at work. Time was a very precious commodity to my father and he generally arranged for me to do something else in the meantime.

Gradually, a system evolved whereby I cycled the two miles home from school, ate a three-course lunch, rode the horse or horses to the blacksmith, then sprinted the 600 yards to school. All this in seventy-five minutes.

Looking back I don't know how I managed it, but I was rarely late. Returning after school, I would read over some homework, the horses being so familiar with the road that they needed no guidance from me.

I fondly remember one lively strawberry roan mare. Norah had been on the racetrack but she was not fast enough and eventually landed up between the shafts of our milk cart. Blessed with a lovely action, she was a dream to ride. That mare was so keen on speed that we never had recourse to a whip or stick in the 10 years we owned her.

Saddles were a luxury unknown on our farm so we always rode bareback — even when wearing a kilt or short breeks. If the horse was sweating on the run in, the sweat used to sting my legs like billy-oh when it dried. I recall some uncomfortable history lessons in springtime when the horse was casting its winter coat.

Although I liked history, the teacher seldom got my undivided attention while I picked horse hair off my bare legs.

Our school boasted an outstanding maths teacher who was also a ferocious disciplinarian. She was the only person ever to put the fear of death into me. Now, my grasp of algebra left much to be desired, with the result that the formidable lady was never slow to keep me in after school. Sure enough, this once happened on an afternoon when I had a horse at the smiddy.

To get even, I arranged with a pal to collect the horse from the blacksmith and tie it to the railings below the classroom window. His task accomplished, up came the shout: "That's yer horse, Hamish. I'm off!" The teacher took one look out of the window and snapped: "Get that brute out of here." She never kept me in again. And my algebra never did improve much.

Shoeing old, canny horses presented no problem for the blacksmith. But trying to shoe colts for the first time was a different matter. I remember helping two smiths restrain a young mare that was being broken in. We all suffered a good kicking in the process of getting her first set of shoes on. Although she eventually turned out a quiet beast in all traffic, she always did hate her bi-monthly visit to the smiddy.

If all went well, a blacksmith could shoe four horses in a forenoon and another four in the afternoon. The daily throughput was often reduced, however, by the extra time spent on complicated cases. For example, horses continually worked on hard roads frequently developed leg and foot troubles whch needed particular care and, occasionally, special shoes.

It was excruciatingly boring to stand for an hour each day in the middle of a burn to let the horses cool their feet and ankles. Could that performance be the origin of the phrase: "We'll let him cool his heels for a while?" Mind you, the cold-water cure certainly works. Recently, I slipped in the dairy parlour and sprained my wrist trying to break the fall. My son promptly handed me the cold-water hose. The icy spray on the pulsating wrist was agony, but it produced a swift, effective cure.

Anyway, I am fortunate to have a blacksmith who is still willing to work at farmers' rates. It is always a relief to hear him say he can fix it. He is part genius, past master craftsman and large part plain obligng.

And I hope he reads the "Farm Journal".

Passion for poultry

A letter from my sister last week brought memories flooding back.

She tells me that she and her two sons are setting up a 7,000-bird free-range unit on their farm in the Midlands. Work is well advanced and already contracts have been signed with two supermarket chains to purchase all these free-range eggs.

The letter did not specify just how much liberty the hens will enjoy. I do not think, for example, that the houses will be moved from field to field as ours were.

Still, most farms did have some permanent henhouses where the birds were allowed outside. That practice was all very well when, as was the rule on most farms, the hens were numbered in hundreds. But if we are thinking in terms of thousands . . . well, the mind boggles. The mud generated in a wet winter by all those feet would swamp many acres.

The invention of battery cages for laying hens was the worst thing that ever happened to farming. The concentration of laying birds into huge battery units spelt the beginning of the end for mixed farming — a system which used to be the backbone of the Scottish farming industry.

I liked hens, although I never kept more than 400 layers at any one time. Constant attention to detail was essential, from the arrival of the boxes of day-old chicks, right through to the final dispatch of the old hens two years later. However, a well-kept unit, stocked with a good laying strain, provided satisfactory reward for the work.

An old neighbour used to swear by a light breed of pure white Leghorns; but I preferred a cross-bred hen with a well-fleshed breast and a heavier carcase to sell at the end of the day. Into this category came Rhode Island red, cross white Leghorn and a light Sussex cross brown Leghorn. This latter combination involved the heavy breed of hen being crossed with a cockerel of the light breed.

Intriguingly, these two crosses of birds were sex-linked, even as day-old chicks. The females of the cross sported feathers of a different colour from the males. It was very handy to discover immediately you opened the lid of the chicken box whether you had pullet or cockerel chicks.

Sometimes I had pure Wyandottes. They were a very docile breed; but it was about eight weeks before you could tell how many pullets or cockerels you had in the batch.

The origins of these breeds is a subject which has always fascinated me. Rhode Island (red), Plymouth (Rock), Leghorn (white) and Wyandotte — these are all places on the eastern seaboard of the US. It would seem that the European settlers improved on the breeds they took to the New World, then exported them back to Europe.

I intend to find out more about this before I'm much older. The transatlantic airlines are desperately seeking passengers this year (fancy being able to fly across the Atlantic for less than £200!) and back in

November I bought some dollars when the exchange rate was $2 to the £.

Today, the pound buys only one dollar, 70 cents, so every time I spend $7 I will have one free. I am looking forward to delving in libraries in the Eastern States to investigate the region's early poultry industry.

A wonderful camaraderie flourished among poultry keepers. Tricks of the trade were readily shared by the men and women involved. It was a matter of pride to lose as few chicks as possible in the rearing. Plenty farmers' wives could boast on 100 eight-month-old pullets, reared from 100 day-old chicks delivered. I never attained that. But I did pride myself on my skill at culling, that is, picking out the unhealthy and non-laying pullets.

My level of ability was far surpassed. however, by Mr Hibbard, a wizard who had a mastery of all things pertaining to poultry. His background I never learned. He was in his 60s, an experienced chicken sexer and an expert at culling.

I particularly remember one visit when from my laying flock of 400 birds he picked out 46. I was peeved and reckoned that for once he had gone over the score.

Normally, the poultry merchant would come and buy the non-layers within three days of notification, but this time I was determined to prove Mr Hibberd wrong. I kept them in isolation for a fortnight. In that time I got a grand total of five eggs — and six of the hens dropped dead. I never questioned his expertise again.

During the 1950s, free range was gradually superseded by the deep-litter system. Well-run deep-litter houses worked efficiently, especially in winter when eggs were dearest. We used electricity to extend the daylight hours and thus stimulate egg production.

The 60s saw the introduction of battery cages. All other hen-keeping systems quickly became redundant or uneconomical. Today, most hens in Britain are kept in specialist units and confined in cages with automatic egg collection. Almost inevitably, there has been increasing public outcry against the intensive form of egg production, hence the start of a swing back to free range.

Personally, I would welcome the return of modest-sized flocks to farms. My ideal number would be 300-600 birds. But how does one manage 7,000 under such a system? I shall wait and see.

Doubtless, today's breeds of hen will adapt to the new conditions. But where will we find today's hen-wives? We have bred a generation of young women and men who have lost those skills which their parents and grandparents took for granted.

I do not doubt that young farm people could quickly learn old techniques. However, the big question is: Will they want to go back to plowtering in the dubs, hens' pail in one hand and egg basket in the other, in the teeth of a winter gale?

Taking a second over soup course

I never take seconds. More than 30 years ago, I resolved never to have second helpings. If pressed, I politely, but firmly, refuse.

Yet, there I was the other week, breaking my own rule because of a plate of soup. I was attending a sale at Paisley Market and, after a long, early-Morning drive from the North and a long stand at the ring, the hunger pangs set in with a vengeance. But, it wasn't the fact that I needed the second plateful that made me break my resolution. No, it was the sheer excellence of the broth.

Lots of chefs, cooks and housewives produce good soup, but only three times in my life have I come across soup-makers who have netted five stars. The third time was that day in Paisley.

As a schoolboy, I often used to eat lunch at a boarding house run by my aunt. She was the first outstanding soup-maker I knew. Whatever the variety of soup on offer, the taste was always exquisite. The high standard was maintained over the 30 to 40 lunches served each day.

On the back of her Aga, my aunt kept a huge stockpot, generously filled with large bones. These she replaced twice weekly. Her fishman had a steady order for two cod heads per week — one for each fill of the stockpot. The mixture of beef, and fish stock gave her soup a consistently good foundation.

The second soup-maker par excellence was the Zulu cook to a family in Grahamstown, South Africa. Husband and wife were practising lawyers. They befriended me during my bomb-aimer training at the nearby airfield and most of my weekends were spent at their home. When I arrived on a Friday afternoon, the cook would invite me to the kitchen for a cup of tea. I used to sit talking to her as she prepared the evening meal.

She, too, had a stockpot, but there was always lots of meat on the bones she used. It was ox-meat from the beautiful red Afrikander cattle that pulled the wagons and field implements on the farms in Cape Province. These bullocks, or oxen, were yolked at three years old, worked for three or more years before reaching full maturity, then sold for slaughter. So, the Zulu cook had mature, tasty meat as a basis for her soup.

I never discovered whether her skills were innate or whether they were taught, but she worked to a very definite rule. Whatever she proposed to boil, she lightly roasted first. And what was to be roasted, was duly boiled lightly beforehand. Her roast beef and roast fowl were out of this world.

This method was faithfully adhered to by the cook in her soup-making. Her chopped vegetables were lightly roasted in a frying pan, then added to the soup pot. I always use this tip myself, but I can never quite attain that special taste.

My pot always contains a ham bone for lentil soup or a knuckle bone for broth. I simply cannot abide "bare" broth, that is, soup made without stock or meat. Regrettably, that flavourless concoction is served in too many hotels and restaurants these days.

Sometimes I use beef cubes as well as bone stock to enhance the taste. Why is this necessary? It's because our North-east butchers sell only prime cattle under two years old. They pride themselves on the excellence of their meat, but it is too young to have a rich, full flavour. The old cows from our farms finish up in the Central Belt of Scotland; and doubtless the mart soup I so enjoyed had been made with cow beef, or cow bones.

Similaly, if you wish to taste real mutton broth, you have to go to Dingwall and all points north and west from there. Up that way, people appreciate the superior flavour of mature ewe mutton, as opposed to the tender lamb or hogget which we eat in the affluent North-east. Sadly, the days have gone when a farmer could kill the odd pig or old ewe for his own use.

Nowadays, it is easy to freeze soup for later use. I must say, I prefer "yaval" broth to first day's. That lovely word "yaval" is not heard nearly as much as it used to be. It means of course, second day's, or second-time round. The soup seems to mature on the second day.

The word "yaval" brings back memories of the last time I attended the Paris Show. It was in spring, 1974. I was in a group that included the late Willie Sharp, of Castleton, King Edward. Willie was a delightful character and great company. He had us all in stitches when he came down to breakfast on the last morning and announced in his booming voice: "Dammit boys! I've hid tae yaval a sark the day." I shall not translate.

I think I shall go back to Paisley Mart again shortly. Not for the soup, you understand. I will persuade my son that we need a young Friesian bull to replace the old one, since he is now coming back on to his own stock.

Once there, maybe I could have a word with the cook about her secret ingredient for that broth. Maybe I'll come back with a bit of cow beef on the bone. And, maybe some day, my soup will be as good as the best.

JULY 1991

When hen fever gripped the US

There are two kinds of Americans — those who are farmers and wish that they weren't and those who aren't farmers and wish that they were. At least, that was the impression I got on my recent visit to the US.

I travelled many hundreds of miles, but concentrated mainly on Virginia and North and South Carolina. These states were the favoured destinations for a sizeable proportion of the Scots who emigrated in their thousands from the mid to late 18th century, the period when Highland crofters were cleared off the land to make way for sheep.

The emigrants found the soil of Virginia and the Carolinas much more fertile than that of their native Scottish highlands. With perseverance and a share of good luck, many of them succeeded in growing a wide variety of crops. And the numerous creeks, inland lakes and sea lochs provided an abundance of seafood. Probably the chief hazard for the Scottish settlers was the mosquito. Certainly, malaria took a heavy toll on the new arrivals in the early years.

During my time there in late May, early June, the temperature remained in the upper 80s. As I am no great lover of a blazing sun, I confined my sightseeing to the early mornings and the comparative cool of the evenings. At the height of the day, I would be safely ensconced in an excellent air-conditioned public library, at a desk covered with books on the subjects that interest me.

I have nothing but praise for the excellence of the library service we enjoy here in Grampian, but it is, I'm afraid, poor relation to the American facilities I experienced. The computers in cities such as Norfolk, Virginia, and Charleston, South Carolina, quickly produced the book I was looking for.

I have a great hankering to work a computer myself and I'm seriously considering enroling for a course of instruction at the BEST centre here in Buckie next winter. Incidentally, the marvels of computerisation were really brought home to me the other day when, with not so much as a blip, the computer at our local library was able to let my son know which books by Dick Francis he had not yet read.

Well, armed with a battery of modern technology, the American librarian could not have been more helpful to me in my quest for information about the early development of the nation's poultry industry. The facts I gathered help to explain why it is that chicken remains to this day one of the American's favourite dishes.

Back in the mid 19th century there started a craze for poultry breeding — a craze which developed into a cult, much as the cult of Elvis Presley has flourished in our times. Peoples from all walks of life took to chicken breeding. Soon, every community had its poultry fanciers' club and ultimately individual states established associations of fanciers' clubs.

Each club had its own preferred poultry breeds. Strains of prolific layers

82

were developed and these compared against each other in strictly controlled tests. Egg production was meticulously recorded.

In the 1850s and 60s, the phenomenon was described as "hen fever". Everyone except tenement dwellers could indulge in the hobby because most houses were set in a maximum of a quarter block, providing ample room for poultry keeping. Lawyers, preachers, businessmen, tradesmen, farmers and housewives all vied with each other to produce a better strain of laying bird.

Qualities such as fine feathering and nice colour markings were studied along with egg producton. Breeders enthused about the beauty of their birds and many newspaper articles were devoted to describing the rooster's magnificent red combs and wattles.

A poultry show held in Boston in 1860 boasted an entry of 8,000 birds. Many of the exotic breeds featured there have disappeared without trace, but there is still a flourishing society for the preservation of rare poultry. Of course, the best breeds, such as Rhode Island Reds, White Wyandottes (named after an Indian tribe) and Plymouth Rocks, have survived. Interestingly, the Light Sussex — which I had always taken to be an English breed — was developed in Sussex County, Virginia. The Warrens were named after Warren County in North Carolina.

All this extensive poultry breeding inevitably gave rise to a lot of culling and so there developed the American passion for fried chicken. I found heaps of old recipes for preparing and cooking chicken in every way imaginable. Sadly, one piece of luggage with my recipe lists inside got on to the wrong Greyhound bus and is still missing.

Today's landless Americans no longer raise chickens, but they do play at farming. On an infinite variety of ride-on mowers they keep cutting, cutting at grass that should be left in peace to grow and provide its roots with some shade against the fierce sun.

The real farmers in the states I visited have to take a job in the nearest town, or drive lorries or buses to subsidise their farming operations. Their grass was at the hay-cutting stage and so was mine when I got back home.

Time called on old meal mill

The news that Hamlyn's mill at Buckie is to close is bad news for me.

North Eastern Farmers has bought our local oatmeal mill and another at Kirriemuir and it plans to close both right away. This is an example of the very worst sort of buy-out, the kind where the buyers' only motive is to crush all potential opposition.

I am particularly annoyed because the mill at Buckie has long been the source of my staple diet — oatmeal. I have been accustomed to buying it in 3kg bags at a very reasonable price.

In the same way as each malt or blended whisky takes its distinctive flavour from the distillery of origin, the taste of oatmeal differs markedly from mill to mill. No doubt the North Eastern Farmers' new oatmeal plant at Boyndie, near Banff, produces excellent meal; and I shall have to get used to it. But what irks me is that the closure of the Buckie mill still further reduces the choice to consumers.

I liked going to the mill about once a month for a fresh supply. An elderly farmer friend of mine, who lives alone, always bought his oatmeal by the half-hundredweight and I doubt if it could have been very fresh by the time he rached the bottom of the bag. There is an awful lot of spoonfuls in 56lb. Seeing him with his huge sack, I teased him about when he expected the chickens to arrive. Oatmeal provides an excellent first feed for day-old chicks and 100 of them would soon use up 56lb.

As I recall, the meal girnal at our farm in pre-war days had a capacity of 5cwt and it was refilled four times a year. Nothing can beat oatmeal as a staple food. Porridge, brose, skirlie, stuffing, oatcakes — all are easily made and very nourishing.

My personal favourite is brose. I confess that I do cheat a bit on the plain oatmeal and salt dish, traditionally served up by the kitchie deems to bothy chiels.

My ingredients are five or six spoonfuls of oatmeal, a shaking of salt, a pinch of pepper, a knob of margarine, and a dip with the end of the spoon into the syrup tin. On to this mixture I pour boiling water, then stir vigorously. I place a plate on top of the bowl, cover with a towel, and leave the brose to steam in their own heat for 10 minutes.

Sometimes I put milk on top before eating, but the lovely nutty flavour can best be tasted on their own. One thing bothers me about brose, though. If we sup porridge, we sup "it". If we eat brose, we sup "them". So, can someone please tell me why brose is always plural?

I suppose my interest in oatmeal began when, as a small boy, I used to holiday at Crooksmill, where my uncle, John Grant, was the "miller". He took infinite care with the whole process of milling, from the moment the oats came in at the mill door, to the day when the sweet-smelling sacks of oatmeal finally left the premises.

In his heyday, he enjoyed a lucrative trade providing pinhead meal, which was transported by rail to Glasgow for steaming and rolling out flat into oat flakes and porage oats.

In post-war years, the demand for oat products fell away badly. It is gratifying to see that the decline has been arrested. Indeed, oat flakes are now the basis of virtually every health food and breakfast cereal.

Like many other farmers, I gave up growing oats and concentrated on wheat and barley. This switch had its disadvantages because young calves will nibble bruised oats at an earlier age than they will tackle crushed barley, so I decided about five years ago to include a few acres of oats in my cropping programme.

Imagine my surprise last autumn when I found merchants willing to take all the oats I could supply — this at a time when the market for barley was sluggish.

The proportion of husk to kernel being higher in oats than in other cereals, my uncle's mill produced two useful by-products from the oatmeal-making process.

The first was sids, or outer husks. These went for grinding into cattle feed. Secondly, there was pron — the inner husks with oat meal dust clinging to them. These were steeped in a vast tin bath until all the flour sank to the bottom.

The cloudy liquid was then carefully preserved in stone jars and used in the winter to make sowens. When boiled, the sowens quickly set into a greyish, unattractive mush that had a somewhat bitter taste. I never really liked them, but they were cetainly nutritious and seemed to keep away the 'flu. My uncle, the miller, was very partial to gruel, also made from oatmeal. Unfortunately, I don't remember how it is prepared.

Any mention of porridge always reminds me of Polly, an elderly spinster who used to be our babysitter in the 60s. One Sunday at lunchtime, she announced: "Dinna gie me a big helping o' meat, Mr Watt. I made porridge for ma brakfaist the day and I made ower much. But I just took ma time and wore through it."

I'm sure that says something for the character of North-east folk. Many a time when I have a tedious task to perform or a long journey to undertake I remember Polly. I just take my time and wear through it.

There are aye changes, but some changes we could do without. I am sure the good folk of Kirriemuir and of Buckie will miss the familiarity and regret the passing of their own local meal mill.

Close call revives memories

A house-for-sale advert caught my eye the other day.

It was for 68b on a certain street in Keith. The "b" indicated that the property might be in a close. so I checked when passing through the town.

The sight of the house transported me back 50 years to a Saturday in autumn, 1939.

On that day there was great activity in the streets of Keith because the Gordon Highlanders Territorials were marshalling to move south by train from the local schools where they had been mustered and billeted for several weeks.

Saturdays were our busiest day on the milk delivery round and my father was well behind schedule. Already an hour late home for its lunchtime bran mash, his horse was becoming restive. Hunger was kittling it up.

We had a lot of customers in the area of troop activity. Since many of our customers' houses were near a busy junction, our horse was led into a close to be clear of the traffic. Access to the upstairs flats was by stout wooden stairs and wooden platforms in front of the doors which were at least 10ft up.

We milk delivery boys — "trotters" as we were commonly called — often worked ahead of the horse and milk cart. This practice was particularly useful when, as on that Saturday, we were running late with the deliveries.

And so it came about that our horse was momentarily alone when the pipe band leading a contingent of soldiers to the station decided to strike up again.

The horse took fright and bolted through the mouth of the close. It whirled round and the hub of the cart wheel caught the bottom step of the wooden stair, bringing the whole caboodle rickling down.

Racing out of the close, the horse headed straight across the main road and into a street where we lads were working. I instinctively started running in the same direction and, as the horse drew alongside me, I managed with no great difficulty to grab the shaft of the cart and then the reins.

Although very young I was well accustomed to dealing with runaways.

With the animal firmly under control, I returned to the close — and confronted a scene of devastation. What had been a solid stairway was now a twisted mess of broken spars.

The lady of the house came to the door and found herself stranded 10ft up.

Although the affair was tragic, we young milk loons also found it very funny. Needless to say, the lady did not appreciate our warped sense of humour. In fact, she got quite mad.

My father took ages to persuade a master joiner to organise a squad of men to repair the stair that afternoon.

However, so long as nobody got hurt, we were inclined to take such accidents in our stride.

Recently, I had the good fortune to meet again my first girlfriend. Despite parental disapproval, we had courted for several years. The decades between quickly evaporated as we reminisced about those wartime days.

She reminded me of another encounter I had with a runaway horse. We were out walking together when the peace was shattered by a commotion behind us.

A driverless horse pulling a gig was coming at full gallop. I dashed up the road and when the horse came alongside, I succeeded in grabbing the shaft and then the reins.

I quietened the animal while my girlfriend pacified the two terrified children in the gig. It was a much-relieved father who arrived on the scene to find that his youngsters were unscathed.

My old flame also laughingly recalled the Saturday night I turned up for our date two-and-a-half hours late. We had arranged to meet at the library at 7 pm. However, at that precise moment, I was at the head of a hill trying to calve a Friesian heifer.

With today's simple but effective calving machines, I could have attached the soft ropes to the calf's feet and gently eased it into the world, one ratchet notch at a time. In the 40s, no such facility existed and the only calving aid available was brute force — mine.

Have you tried to find someone to help you on a farm at 7 o'clock on a Saturday evening? Usually, the place is deserted — and so it was that night. Sometimes it needed three strong men to get a calf out, but there was only me, one strong youth.

I had managed to get ropes on the legs of the calf and had attached them to a stout shaft which I proceeded to pull. To make matters worse, the heifer would not lie down, otherwise I could have stuck one end of the shaft in the earth and used it as a lever.

An hour went by and still the calf's head had not emerged, although it was perfectly placed in the birth channel.

Two hours went by — the heifer was going done and so was I. Desperate measures were called for if I was to get that calf out alive. I took them.

Manoeuvring the exhausted cow close to a fence post, I took the ropes off the shaft and tied them securely round the post. Then I gave the heifer a smack on the ribs with the shaft I had in my hand.

The beast got such a fright that it staggered forward and out shot the calf, none the worse and gasping for its first breath. It took quite some time to persuade the heifer to return to the scene of the birth and start licking her calf.

That is why I was late for my date. It seemed a good reason to me, but my girlfriend was less than pleased. Still, I suppose no lassie likes playing second-fiddle to a Friesian cow.

War declared on grassland moles

Is there any strychnine in the house? To be precise, is there any strychnine locked away in the poisons cupboard inside the padlocked shed where the sprays are kept?

I've got to go to war against these moles. In a mistaken fit of live and let live last winter, I didn't call in the molecatcher. In the past few days, I have paid dearly for it.

Every spring we carefully use a land leveller and link harrows to eliminate the countless mole heaps scattered over the grassland. This is followed by a slow roll with a heavy roller filled with water to give extra weight.

On our farmyard we make a lot of FYM — farmyard manure. Liberal top dressings of grassland with this muck produce thousands of healthy worms. These fat juicy lunches lead in turn to a healthy population of moles — the gentlemen in black velvet suits".

I've been calling them something very different this summer. The beggars have been at work again since we levelled the ground and their molehills have played havoc with the mower. Earth and small stones do not make good silage.

Counting the first and second cuts of silage, plus 50 acres of good hay, a total of 250 acres are cut each year. That calls for a good, reliable mower. The £3,000 we forked out for a new machine should be an expense spread over several seasons. With a lot to cut and no time for breakdowns, there is no point in buying a second-hand mower. They deteriorate quickly enough from new.

A mower's moving parts rotate at 2,000 revolutions per minute, so, if it strikes a stone or molehill, serious damage can be done before the power drive of the tractor is switched off and the machine stopped. One molehill can cause the mower to grunt and slow down. A whole series of them can bring it to a screaming halt, amid the horrible smell of burning rubber as the driving belts take the strain.

The mixture of earth and small stones that the little devils throw up with their front feet can be devastating. It is said that their front feet and legs act as both pick-axe and shovel. From the line of abandoned mowers behind my dyke (kept there for spares), anyone would think that an army of Irishmen with pick-axes and shovels had been at work. Incidentally, there are no moles in Ireland. Maybe St Patrick banished them from the land when he got rid of the snakes.

I have often bought mole traps at roups and tried a do-it-yourself job. The traps are spring-loaded with a metal tongue the size of a 50p piece, which protrudes into the middle of the mole run. The mole. which has poor eyesight, is supposed to touch the tongue with its snout, thereby releasing the spring. I have always followed the instructions faithfully. For instance, I have worn gloves to mask the human scent and I've tried to avoid standing on the main runs. I cannot claim any great success, however. Yet, in the hands of an experienced molecatcher, traps can be effective.

I have read that placing evil-smelling materials in the main runs sometimes induces the moles to clear out an go elsewhere. Remedies suggested include mothballs, carbide, even bad fish. But I live in Buckie. How am I supposed to lay my hands on bad fish?

I would really like to catch a mole soon. In ancient folklore, it is claimed that if a mole's front legs are dried and carried in the pocket they will ward off rheumatism. I have promised to present the first pair I find to Charlie Allan to help his rheumaticky knees.

Personally, I still swear by flannel as the best cure for rheumatism. Sad to say, my old flannel square is threadbare from frequent usage and repeated washing. Worse still, I can't find a shop that sells the stuff. Maybe before long I'll have to try the mole's feet myself.

The mole's natural enemies are owls, weasels and stoats — all of which are in short supply in my area. The disappearance of farm stackyards with their resident mouse populations has led to a marked decline in the number of owls. And the open fields, where the moles create most damage, provide little natural cover for weasels or stoats.

Mole control is best undertaken from November to April when the animals are working near the surface. At other times, they delve deep down into the moist soil which harbours the worms. In this wet summer it's a wonder they aren't all working on the surface.

Experts agree that strychnine is the only truly effective weapon against moles. Permits to buy it are closely controlled by the Department of Agriculture's officers, who insist that supplies are kept under lockfast conditions at all times. Thankfully, I have never heard of an accident involving this deadly poison.

There is nothing complicated about using strychnine. Worms are simply dipped in the powder and dropped into the main runs, resulting in instant death for the unsuspecting mole. As moles are cannibals, one poisoned worm can be expected to kill several. But there's aye a snag. The blighters seldom travel more than 200yd from their base, so that dozens of poisoned worms are needed to clear a field.

I wish I could persuade my old molecatcher to come out of retirement, but there's nae chance. Last time I met him his rheumatism was "afa bad".

Gunning for feathered marauders in the field

I always fancied riding shotgun on a stagecoach. From my seat in the one shilling and nine pence back balcony of our local picture house, I enjoyed many a Cowboy and Indian film. The crackshot, rifle slung across his knees, sat beside the stagecoach driver and guarded passengers and bullion.

With the horses at full gallop and the whole coach swaying wildly, the rifleman would pick off attacking Indians one by one as they rode alongside, always with a couple of feathers sticking up from their hair.

Well, there are plenty of feathered marauders in my part of the country. So here I am with a .22 rifle slung across my knees, all right. But I'm sitting on a straw bale in a stationary farm bogie. Overhead, there's a black plastic cover to keep me hidden. I'm guarding nothing more exciting than a field of winter barley which has become the target for every pigeon and crow in the locality.

Many of my neighbours have stopped growing winter barley because of vermin damage, preferring to depend on a spring sowing. As most fields of spring barley ripen at about the same time, the birds' ravages are more widely spread.

However, we still like to have at least one field of winter barley so that an early start can be made to the harvest. This has the advantage of ensuring that all the machinery is in working order after the year-long lay-up.

Moreover, we can use the new barley as the first supplement for the dairy cows. By early August, the high feeding value of early spring grass is diminishing and a feed of rolled barley at milking time helps to keep up the cows' milk supply. Once a cow starts to slide from her peak yield, it is difficult to arrest the decline.

On this farm, we study closely the daily meter readings left by the milk tanker driver. Comparing the total litres collected day-by-day, we are able accurately to assess the overall trend in milk yield.

This year, our winter barley is Manitou, a six-rowed variety, supposedly resistant to bird damage. Yet from where I sit I can see that the crows in particular have developed a crafty method of getting at what they want. The technique is to land on an individual barley stem, causing it to break. When the barley head subsequently bends down, the bird is able to attack the bottom of the head, thus avoiding the bristling awns. Oor craws are nae daft.

Serious bird damage begins when the barley seed is at the milky stage, about 14 days before the crop is ready to combine. Once the seed ripens and hardens, the birds go elsewhere. The more the sun shines, the sooner my stint will end. I'm no great shot, after all. In fact, I don't much like guns and I welcome anyone prepared to help kill the birds or at least scare them away.

For three successive years, I was blessed with the superb services of an airman from the Kinloss base. He was a country man from deepest Devon and he had an accent to match. Arriving at daybreak, just after 4.00am, he would meticulously construct his hide with camouflage netting and barley stalks, then set out a dozen decoy pigeons before retreating to the hide.

Scarcely had he settled in when pigeons and crows would come winging down for their first feed of the day. On his very best day he bagged 162 pigeons and a couple of dozen crows in the space of 14 hours. At the end of three days, the pigeon menace was eradicated for that year.

I miss Fred, because it is always a pleasure to see a real expert at work. And best practice is something that can be passed on to young people.

It was for this reason that, in my capacity as chairman of Grampian education committee, I encouraged the establishment of a course for gamekeepers at Clinterty college. I know that this type of course has been established at Thurso college, but conditions at Strathnaver or Forss are somewhat different from those in Strathdon or Forres.

There are enough estates in Grampian to provide a steady stream of 12 to 15 young gamekeepers for a course extending over one or two years. Now that the new combined college structure is in place, I hope that tuition in these country skills will soon be introduced.

Meanwhile, my gun makes plenty of noise; but if the film-makers were depending on me for their supply of head feathers, precious few cowboy and Indian films would appear. Mind you, they don't really make them like that anymore. Nowadays, the American indians do not appreciate being referred to as "red Indians", nor do they like being portrayed as perpetual losers.

If those whom I met this summer in Virginia are typical of their race, they are a very handsome people. The men are strong-featured and athletic looking. The women are quite lovely. Their skin is the exact colour of a ripe chestnut with the soft, dewy sheen of the kernel when newly opened. I'd barter my rifle for one any day.

Caught up in American razzmatazz

My visit to America in the early summer was principally taken up with studying the present state of agriculture and the past history of the country's poultry industry. But the memory that keeps coming most often to mind is of the half-day I spent in Washington, sharing with millions the spectacular military parade celebrating victory in the Aarabian Gulf.

I was en route north to Boston for a Sunday morning flight to Scotland. My Greyhound bus arrived in Washington at 5 am on Saturday, the day of the parade. So, instead of catching a connecting bus straight through, I took a cab to Constitution Avenue, where the event was due to start at 11am.

Had the parade taken place in London, the crowds would have been positioned many hours beforehand. But to my surprise, I arrived among the first of the spectators, in time to see the city workmen hanging huge yellow ribbons from every lamp post and house front. I chose a pavement seat about 100yd ahead of the Presidential saluting base.

Constitution Avenue is a beautiful wide tree-lined boulevard, stretching in a straight line for three miles. From early morning, police helicopters patrolled it and the surrounding streets, then at 9am the police force arrived.

They were equipped with every imaginable mode of transport, including electric vehicles that looked for all the earth like milk delivery trucks and moved at the same slow speed. The policemen and women were themselves all shapes and sizes — but mostly fat. Their general attitude was very casual and good humoured.

Patriotic music and welcome-home messages to the troops blared from countless public address systems along the route. I got the impression that America doesn't really know where history ends and Hollywood begins. I should hate to be an American school kid. You could never be sure it was General MacArthur or John Wayne who won the war in the Pacific.

And yet, in their own way, the Yanks are good at spectacle — pageantry, no, but spectacle, certainly. Spot on 11 o'clock, lorries and jeeps full of film and TV cameramen appeared. Then came the mightily impressive procession of fighting men and women. Nearly 10,000 of them there were — row after row, 12 abreast, filling the entire three miles of the avenue by the time the march reached its conclusion two hours later.

A huge variety of sophisticated fighting equipment was on display, some of it on public view for the first time. Overhead, Army and Navy helicopters and fixed-wing aircraft from the US Air Force kept up a constant fly-past. Small wonder that Saddam Hussein's soldiers had shown little stomach for a fight against such well-armed troops.

But, America being America showbiz is never far away. So help me, there in the midst of all that deadly weaponry were two decorated floats with jazzy musicians on board.

Normally, I am not easily impressed by "spectacular"; but the phalanx of flags from the 23 countries which sent troops to the Gulf forcefully brought home to me how truly international the armies of "Desert Storm" had been.

With 30,000 servicemen and women involved, Britain had the second largest number of personnel in the war. Their contribution to the victory was duly acknowledged by every announcer.

The United States band, 200 strong and resplendent in white uniforms, got the biggest cheer of the day. Their dazzling whites contrasted strongly with the sand-coloured uniforms and boots worn by the rest of the troops. For myself, though, the real highlight was the US marine band. They halted directly in front of me for several minutes because of some hitch up ahead. As they moved off again, they struck up their anthem — you know, the one that goes: "From the halls of Montezuma to the shores of Tripoli". Well! There was I, a cynical Scotsman; cheering loudly with the best of them and thoroughly enjoying the infectious razzmatazz.

The hold-up in the parade, together with the sight of decorated floats, brought back memories of another, more modest parade. Back in the mid-1950s, the Keith gala committee organised an evening pageant of decorated floats and cars. More than 50 vehicles turned out.

I participated, along with the quietest cow I ever owned. She stood on an open lorry with no sides, tied only by a halter, while I sat on a three-legged stool milking her by hand into a wooden bucket. Occasionally, I would direct a squirt of milk towards the children along the route.

My brother's float followed, an all-stainless-steel display depicting modern milk production. The children lining the streets all received free samples of the finished product — ⅓pint carton of flavoured milk.

It had been decided that the parade should be led by a horse-drawn carriage. By chance, I still had a mare that had pulled a milk cart before our switch to motor transport two years previously. And so Bess was pressed into service for the evening, despite the fact that her girth had increased to such an extent that she could hardly squeeze between the shafts.

The three gala organisers were a hotelier, a banker and a master electrician. None of them had ever handled a horse before, but off they set, not knowing "weesh" from "hi" (left from right in horseman's language). Fortunately, Bess was quiet and biddable.

With half the route completed, everything was going well when suddenly we all came to a dead stop. The problem was a mystery to me because the head of the parade was round the corner out of sight. Several minutes later, some young lads came racing along the line of floats shouting for me to come at once. I rounded the corner and burst out laughing.

Remembering her milk-round days, Bess had halted at a house where she used to get a daily slice of loaf. She had mounted the pavement, carriage and all, and was rattling at the door knob with her teeth, demanding her piece. The amateur drivers could not budge her.

Before I reached the scene, the lady owner of the house, who had been standing some distance away, recognised her old friend and ran home. Out she came with a clap and some bread for the mare; and only then did Bess condescend to move again, allowing the pageant to proceed.

The organisers were somewhat crestfallen and decidely not amused. But och, they numbered only three. For me and for the many dozens of other folk who saw the incident, it was fairly the big highlight of the evening.

Healing powers of flannel

I'm rich, I'm rich. I haven't won the football pools or been lucky at "Fix the ba". I've had a better windfall than that — a present of a new piece of flannel, 30in by 24.

Doubled, it fits over the hip perfectly. Single, it's the ideal cover for my back.

This past month's dry, warm weather has been a godsend to farmers, helping to make top-quality hay of the later cuts of grass. The early part of the harvest has been quite equally fortunate and very little of the winter barley will need expensive artificial drying.

But there's aye a something. I managed to be caught in the one and only downpour of the prolonged dry spell. One evening I was rowing grass, two bouts into one, when the heavens opened. My tractor has no cab, only a safety-frame, so within minutes I was soaked. By the time I got from the far end of the silage field back to the steading the water was literally running out of the back of my breeks.

When I climbed off that tractor, there wasn't a dry bit on my body. And worse was to come. There in the calving field, close by the steading, a Friesian heifer was in the process of giving birth. I decided to wait for a few minutes to assist her.

As often happens on such occasions, the minutes stretched into two hours, by which time I had got a proper "stervin". A strong whisky and a hot bath helped to drive out the cold; but sure enough, two evenings later my hips started to stoun.

I consider myself fortunate to be as free of rheumatism as I am. It's all thanks to the healing properties of flannel — proven over many years. A few weeks back, I was lamenting the fact that my old faithful flannel patch had worn out.

I am extremely grateful to Farm Journal reader Mrs Ruth Gatt, Bagrae, Alvah, who took pity on me and kindly sent this new piece. In an accompanying note, she tells me it was cut from a web which was in the house when she moved in. It is of closer weave than my old rag and should, therefore, stand up to wear and washing for quite a time.

After wearing my gift constantly for three days, my aches and pains disappeared, as I knew they would. That is why I am feeling rich and contented. So, Mrs Gatt, please accept my grateful thanks. Incidentally, her parcel also contained a piece of flannel for me to pass on to Charlie Allan. Here's hoping it works for him as well as it does for me.

Shortly after I wrote the article on moles. I chanced across a newly-dead specimen. Having removed the front legs and carefully dried them in the sun, I intend to present them, along with the flannel, to Charlie to see if he can cure his arthritic knees.

As I mentioned before, I cannot personally vouch for the efficacy of dried moles' feet in warding off rheumatism. However, the claim certainly creeps up repeatedly in folklore throughout Britain.

Mrs Gatt's flannel is very old and this is probably good news because it is less likely to contain man-made fibres. The nap is brushed on both sides of the material and these short fibres create a perfect air trap between the material and the skin of the wearer.

Many a person remembers having to wear flannel as a small child and hating the itchiness it caused. I understand the material was greatly favoured for fishermen's vests.

Farm baillies, or cattlemen, also liked it. Sweating indoors for several hours, as he fed and mucked his cattle, the baillie was often called upon to go to the turnip field for an hour or two before lowsing time.

The temperature change from an overwarm byre to the sometimes bitter cold of a neep park meant that sweat cooled on his back and made him vulnerable to a chill. If, however, he was wearing a flannel linner, it created a warm air barrier next to his skin.

My initial experience of flannel, or flannels came with my first pair of long trousers. Right proud of them I was, too. How I hated shorts, and the kilt was little better. If either got wet, they chaffed the backs of my knees.

With long flannel trousers, and all of 14, I felt I had reached a major milestone in life. The cloth of these trousers was not at all like the material I now prize and I think the term "flannels" must have been purely a trade name.

Since I'm in the business of thanking readers for their help and advice, may I say I am indebted, too, to all those who have written to me about trapping moles.

My blacksmith in Cairnie tells me he had a plague of moles on his croft and garden last spring. He bought new lightweight traps and they were an instant success. The secret, he believes, is to bury these in the ground for few days to eradicate the smell of man. It is then vital to wear gloves at all times when setting the traps in the main mole runs.

It's simple, he assures me; so I will take heart and have another go this back end.

Children not well versed on farming

First the farmer sows his seeds:
Then he stands and takes his ease.
What a shame it is that children should be fed such untruths, even if only in the form a nursery rhyme.

Rhymes are taught to children at a very early age and few forget them, no zatter how inaccurate they are.

Now, if Jack and Jill had gone down the hill to fetch a pail of water it would have been believable. Anyone who has ever carried water knows that the well is usually at a much lower level than the house.

And when, tell me when, does today's farmer find time to stand and take his ease? The seeds were sown a long time ago. Already we are at the tail-end of harvest and there has been little let-up in between.

Even the arable farmer must pay constant attention to his crops. Since the majority of Scottish farmers have both crops and livestock, summer is an extremely busy time. Our animals have to be fed and housed throughout the 220-day winter. Provision of fodder and bedding for that period allows small respite during our short spring and summer.

There are certainly times when farmers can be seen standing still; but even then they are busy. The recent hot weather has made the newly-home lambs very susceptible to fly-strike. Walking through the flock may reveal nothing, but a few minutes standing still, watching carefully and quietly, can show one lamb twitching its tail rapidly. Also, it may be turning its head towards its tail as if anxious to scratch its rear end.

This lamb must be caught and examined to see if flies have deposited eggs on the mucky part of the fleece. In bad cases, the farmer finds that the eggs have hatched, leaving maggots active on the skin — a condition often indicated by a damp patch on the fleece.

Cleaning away the infestation is a particularly loathsome task, but it must be done immediately with strong disinfectant or sheep dip. Some-times the only answer is to treat the whole flock with fly-repellent dip. The best cure of all is one night's sharp frost to put an end to the fly menace.

One of my vital daily routines is to stand still, watching the dairy cows. Catching cows coming into season and mating them with a specific bull is a constant, time-consuming chore.

Some go to a dairy bull to breed future herd replacements. Others have to be matched to beef bulls.

Some cows are easy to spot. They seek to disturb the whole herd for the 20 hours or so they are in season. Others, again, are really difficult to detect. these are known as silent bullers. They show signs of activity only once every 20 minutes.

Failure to identify them on the day would mean a wait of 21 days before I got the next chance. In these harsh economic times, it is important to get cows to calve within a 12-month period or less. A calving index of more than 365 days can be very costly, resulting in an extended dry period and lost production.

One of the most embarrassing episodes of my farming career happened because I didn't spend enough time taking my ease.

I had bought a bonny blue roan Welsh pony for the children and understood him to be a gelding. He turned out to be a vicious brute, extremely difficult to handle and a thorough nuisance about the place. He put my kids off horses for life — so maybe he did me a favour.

Anyway, after a few weeks of persevering I put him back to a pony sale and was pleased to break even on the transaction. Imagine my horror when the mart phoned next day to say that the beast had been rejected by the buyer because he was a stallion, not a gelding. The man in the office laughed at me for weeks for not having noticed.

When it comes to sheep, I am very fussy about identifying tups and riggs among my lambs. I make it a rule to castrate my bull calves while they are still young. However, I just had not taken the time to examine that pony.

The beast was duly returned and I sent for the vet to do the necessary. That vet did not spare my blushes. Taking me quietly by the sleeve, he said: "Come on and I'll spell it out to you in words of one syllable.

"We will start with the birds and the bees." The pony didn't even kick him for me!

Farm's four-legged fool!

I love the humour of the extremely talented Scotland the What? team.

They can certainly see the funny side of the North-east's farming community. Still, I thought they had exceeded the bounds of credibility when they christened Auchterturra's pub the Glaiket Stirk.

That was, until I got one myself. No, not a pub. I'm not that daft. It's bad enough being a farmer in a recession. But I have got a glaiket stirk.

The poor calf caught an infection of the inner ear when she was about a fortnight old. Despite immediate treatment, his eyes developed a squint and his head and neck twisted so that he wears a permanent quizzical look.

Now this has nothing to do with mad cow disease, or BSE as it is known. Fortunately, I have never seen a case of bovine spongiform encephalopathy and I hope I never do. The veterinary profession has quickly mastered that problem and we can look forward to its complete eradication within a very few years.

My stirk is thriving really well and his coat has a bonny shine. But oh, he is feel!

Instead of drinking milk from the bucket immediately in front of him, he dives for one to the left or the right. Maybe he is cross-eyed. Does he stand head-on to the trough containing his concentrates, as any sensible beast would? Not him — he stands sideways and prevents his mates from feeding.

Rather than pull hay from the haik, he eats off the floor. Requiring much less rest than his companions, he causes constant disturbance by trampling over them in the course of his roaming. It will be interesting to see how he behaves when he is turned out to grass in the spring.

Over the years, I have developed a keen eye for animal health, but I have never seen a cattle beast like this before. Last year, a non-farming neighbour bought a boxer pup that displayed peculiar behaviour. His vet was puzzled and sent it to a dog psychiatrist. Back came the verdict: "That animal has no brain and is, therefore, totally untrainable." The dog cannot distinguish night from day and would bark incessantly were it not sedated.

Back in the 1974-79 Parliament, when I was whip for my small group of 11 MPs, I was obliged to spend long hours on the green benches to ensure my members were called for their fair share of speaking time.

Sometimes, if the subject under debate was of little interest, my stockman's eye would come into play. I would look at my fellow Members of Parliament and assess who was ill, who was likely to die, who would resign, and where the next by-election would be.

I recognised Harold Wilson's illness at a very early stage and I was greatly surprised that the political press failed to notice his rapid decline. I used to be really sorry for him at Prime Minister's question time.

I remember thinking that if I had a stirk as ill as he was I would take it out of that pen to save it being so badly mauled. Had he carried on as Prime Minister for as much as another three months, I'm sure he would have collapsed.

After Sir Harold had rested and recovered a little, he and I had several long chats. I congratulated him on his recovery and told him how he had reminded me of a good cow I had kept one season too long. Although no countryman himself, Sir Harold appreciated the analogy and agreed that he would have collapsed had he not resigned.

Belonging to neither of the two major parties, I could look on both benches dispassionately. I would compare them to two courts of cattle. If I could have taken a pick, I would have chosen from the Labour Party. However, if I'd had to take them all, I would have plumped for the Tories. Sheepmen will get my meaning when I say there was a better top draw in the Labour Party, but just too big a tail.

My thoughts would often progress to the possibility of selecting the best from both groups. Such an amalgamation would make for effective, dynamic government. If the Cabinet were composed of the best brains from all parties, this country might finally get somewhere.

We might, for example, set about curing the idiotic situation whereby Britain imports £6billion of food that could be produced from our own resources. And matters are becoming ever more farcical in the European Parliament, where British Labour and Conservative MEPs don't talk to each other.

Small wonder that Britain and British agriculture get such a poor deal from the EC. There is no point in blaming one party or the other for the debacle. They are equally guilty.

It is hardly surprising that they have concocted the notion of land given over to set-aside — land producing nothing. This is definitely the politics of the madhouse, or of glaiket stirks.

It is surely not beyond the wit of intelligent people to devise a system where party politics come into play only at election times. During the course of a Parliament, MPs should pool their talents to work for the common good. Committees could then be formed comprising members from all parties, proportionate to the number of seats won at the general election.

Under such a system, substantial progress would be ensured. For four years, I served on an investigative committee of that nature and the work was the most productive and satisfying of all my many Parliamentary duties.

We will never get this country out of its economic rut until we get it out of its political rut. That is why the opportunity to establish a different system in Scotland is so attractive.

Westminster is hopelessly bogged down by tradition and glaiket stirks. They are like my bullock — stiff-necked and incapable of seeing straight.

Efficiency puts paid to magic

That's another harvest finished, without even one stook parade.

We have no stooks. Our cereal acreage doesn't really justify having a combine harvester of our own, now that these machines cost more than £100,000. So each year we hire a contractor to cut the lot.

Three visits of the combine spread over about six weeks takes care of the winter barley, followed by the spring barley and then the winter wheat. Last of all comes the oats. This variety of cereal crop helps to avoid harvests that are all bad.

Anyway, this year the grain bins are full, although not heaped as in our best years. The spread of harvest gives us plenty of opportunities to get the straw baled quickly and gathered home in good condition. Our large numbers of cattle depend on it for good feeding and dry bedding.

Last year we tried a new process, treating 200 big bales with ammonia. The cattle loved it and throve on it, so this time we have treated twice as much.

Ammonia-treated straw has a feeding value equivalent to good hay, and it is infinitely preferable to bad hay. Wheat straw, which is very coarse, used to be regarded as fit only for bedding down the cattle courts but now, after treatment, it ranks equally with similarly treated oat and barley straw.

Modern science turns long-held convictions on their heads and we farmers have to adopt and adapt. We must utilise the changes in ways that suit our individual systems.

Nowadays, my involvement with the grain cutting is confined to riding shotgun on the combine, detecting from height where the crop husbandry has gone right and where it has gone wrong. In a weed-free crop there is twice, maybe three times, as much grain as there is in a thin one choked with weeds. Environmentalists please note!

In the days of the binder, you could tell what a crop was like by how close the sheaves lay as they fell. Neighbours and passers-by quickly assessed whether or not you had a good crop by the number of stooks. To make a crop look thicker some farmers would put only eight sheaves to a stook instead of the usual ten.

It was every farmer's ambition to have a field so heavily stooked that he had to reverse the first leading cart into the gateway to make a start. Stories of such crops were in the same category as the fisherman's tale of the big fish that got away.

I used to enjoy stooking. A heavy crop meant the sheaves were a good shape for setting erect. A thin crop could lead to ragged sheaves that were difficult to handle in the stook, on the carts and at the rucks.

There was an art in "biggin' a gweed stook". For instance, when lifting the sheaves it was important to put the binder string knot in the inside of the stook.

This resulted in a close, even top which ran the water much more effectively than an open one. Then, the sheaves had to be given a certain degree of lean, otherwise the stooks were liable to fall over, necessitating a stook parade to re-erect them.

Stook parades usually took place on damp mornings. Oilskin tousers and jackets were vital because every sheaf showered you with water. Harvest times see to be much drier than in the 40s and 50s, when it was very rare to get the crop secured without repeated stook parades.

In a very wet year with poor drying, the stooks often needed turning. The very worst kind of weather was a high wind that scattered the stooks, followed by heavy rain that soaked them through as they lay on the ground.

I used to have a foreman who "didna like a roarin', tearin' win'. Fit we need is a hoochin', soochin', winnin' win'." He stretched his vowels as he said it, almost willing the wind to be just the right strength.

Crops to be cut by combine need to be dead ripe whereas bindered crops were better cut while there was still a touch of green in the stalk. even in an ideal year the sheaves needed about eight days in the stook to allow the grain kernel ro ripen and dry sufficiently.

If the crop was led even slightly damp, the rucks would heat and the grain would mould. It is said that Robbie Burns used mouldy seed one spring and the resultant crop failure forced him out of his farm.

Given reasonable weather, the leading and stacking was, to my mind, the best job of the whole farming year. There was something magical about the "reeshe" of a sheaf as it was forked from the cart to the rapidly rising ruck.

At leading time and stooking time — yes, even at stook parade — there was a camaraderie in the harvest field that has long since disappeared.

No doubt the job of harvesting now gets done more efficiently, but the combine driver has a lonely vigil, perched up there on his expensive metal monster.

Sniper gets bird!

"Slam in the lamb". The advertising slogan of the Scottish Quality Beef and Lamb Association may not be the catchiest ever invented but it certainly contains sound advice, especially this year when lamb in the markets has never been cheaper.

Now is the time to slam in the lamb — into the oven and into the deep freeze. It's even worth filling the freezer compartment of an ordinary fridge. Give yourself a treat while lamb is really cheap. Join with your neighbour of friend to share a lamb.

Prices of lamb (and beef and pork for that matter) have not been reduced in the supermarkets. However, your local family butcher will give you a keen quote for supplying, cutting and packaging a lamb ready for the freezer.

Farmers are receiving only 100-120p a kg for their lambs — say £24 for a 20kg animal. If this Government was really serious about reducing the cost of living and consequently the Retail Prices Index, it, would take action to stop supermarket bosses blatantly profiteering on meat.

Our six top supermarket chains enjoy annual profits which are positively obscene when compared to the huge losses sustained by the primary producer.

Pig farmers are being asked to accept 40% less for their produce this year. Sheep farmers will probably end their year with returns down by 50%.

In addition to the fact that they have not been reimbursed for the inflation factor of 6%, Britain's farmers are forced to carry a huge deflation factor. This at a time when nobody else's prices are being deflated.

Mr John Selwyn Gummer is still, so far as I am aware, the Minister of Food as well as the Minister of Agriculture. It is high time he got to work on narrowing the vast difference in price between what the primary producer receives and what the housewife is asked to pay.

Lamb is a very versatile meat. Roast gigot, saddle of lamb, grilled chops — all are excellent. Then there is the ever delightful lamb hotpots and Irish stews. As well as these traditional dishes, lamb kebabs are a real treat; and it is also quite the best meat for stir fry.

In the winter of 1940, we had an infantry officer billeted and my mother had to provide him with dinner at eight. This was a scutter because we farm folk took our high tea at six. My mother had to set to and prepare his food separately.

One day, he was invited to a shoot and came back with, among other things, a snipe. Why anyone would want to shoot something as tiny as a snipe is beyond me. It may have been that the bird presented a special challenge, due to the fact that in flight it weaves violently from side to side.

The officer asked my mother to hang the bird in the meat safe, saying he would tell her when he required it. At the end of the first week it began to smell and by the beginning of the second week it had to be thrown into the pigs' pail. We all thought he had forgotten about it.

Fifteen days after he had shot it, the officer announced at breakfast that he would like the snipe for dinner that evening. My mother got into a real flap, but after the intitial panic, she firmly resolved to stand her ground and prepare something else really tasty.

When I arrived home from school, she related the sorry tale and suggested I could maybe save the situation by trying my luck at shooting a snipe. Fortunately, about half-a-mile from the house we had a marshy piece of land where snipe fed regularly.

I cannot recall whether I gave the bird a chance to rise, but anyway I bagged one first shot. It was easily plucked as I walked home through the close. A quick singe and clean — and it was ready for the oven.

At nine o'clock that evening I was sitting with half-a-dozen members of the family listening to the news on the wireless when our officer put in an appearance. I see him yet. Poking his blond moustache round the door, he declared: "I just want to congratulate Mrs Watt on the excellent dinner. That was the finest snipe I've ever tasted. You know, it's most important to hang it for precisely the right length of time." We nearly did ourselves an injury trying not to laugh.

I've never shot another snipe since then. In truth, there aren't more than half-a-dozen bites in the wee craiters.

But there is a lot of eating in a lamb. So — see your butcher today. Slam in the lamb.

Poll ends the era of North farming MPs

The outcome of the Kincardine and Deeside by-election was not exactly unexpected.

One interesting fact emerges from it, however. The failure of farmer Mr Marcus Humphrey to retain the seat for the Tories means that for the first time in recent history, probably for the first time ever, there are no farmers representing constituencies in the northern half of Scotland.

Farmers everywhere could be sure that Mr Alick Buchanan-Smith would speak up for the farmers interests. And most importantly, he spoke from a sound knowledge of his subject.

No matter how good a friend to agriculture he may be, a non-farming MP cannot speak with the same authority as a practising farmer. Agriculture is an extremely complex industry, and non-farmers cannot realistically be expected to know all the nuances of legislation affecting it.

Debates on Scottish agriculture in the House of Commons will be the poorer for Alick's passing. In this Parliament there is now only one Scottish member still actively involved in farming — Mr John Home Robertson, Labour MP for East Lothian.

There was an era when the Speaker had difficulty in allocating speaking time to all the Scots' farmer MPs who wished to participate in farming debates. In the 1960s, Caithness and Sutherland was represented by Mr George Mackie. Fortunately, he can still impart his knowledge from the benches of the House of Lords.

Ross-shire's MP was prominent sheep farmer Mr Alistair MacKenzie. At one time, West Aberdeenshire had Mr Jim Davidson for its down-to-earth farm spokesman. That was before he decided to serve the industry as Chief Executive with the Royal Highland Show Society.

In the 1970s, Banffshire and its farmers were represented first by Mr Bill Baker, then by myself and later by Mr David Myles — all farmers.

Farther south there was Mr John Corrie, MP for North Ayrshire and Bute. John could be relied on to add his considerable farming knowledge to the subject. He and I used to study EEC draft regulations with a fine-tooth comb. We spent many a late night in the Chamber, debating their potential effect on the future of Scottish agriculture.

There were also several estate owners on the benches, so perhaps rural affairs were somewhat over-represented.

The Commons contains a large proportion of lawyers and the rest of us used to reckon that they remained lawyers first and MPs second. To be fair, and looking back at it, I suppose we farmers were farmers first and MPs second. Certainly, our interest in agriculture was greater than our interest in petty party politics.

I was often accused by my SNP colleagues of fraternising too much with MPs of other parties. I used to retort that the only way to find out what the opposition was up to was by talking to them.

For a time, I even had a desk in a room with two Welsh Liberal MPs, both of whom were farmers. So maybe cattle and sheep did rather dominate our conversation, much to the disgust of the others who shared the same accommodation.

One autumn I happened to mention to one of the Liberals, Mr Geraint Howells, MP for Cardigan, that the lambs from the hills were extremely dear in the Highlands of Scotland. He volunteered to send me some Welsh lambs from markets in his own constituency.

I wanted 500. When he phoned me at home the following Saturday evening, he said he had bought 720 and that they were aleady on their way north.

With delivery to Banffshire promised by the next day, and the lambs still within my stipulated budget, I thought I was getting a great bargain. They duly arrived, none the worse for their long journey. Healthy little sheep, they were, little bigger than rabbits; and they could run and jump like hares.

Most of the breeds, including my usual North Country Cheviots, run together in a flock when a a sheepdog is sent round them. These Welsh lambs, however, did the opposite and scattered in every direction the minute they saw a dog.

At that time I had an excellent sheepdog I had bred myself. He was a big, strong, wise animal with a lovely dark chocolate coat. Mostly, he knew what was wanted of him, and would work for anyone with a minimum of command. That autumn he was completely dumbfounded, he used to give me a look as if to say: "How am I expected to handle this lot?"

The lambs throve all right, but as there were rather more than I cared to over-winter, I took 200 of them to market in November to sell store. The Welsh sheep had long tails and short, sharp faces, rather like Shetland sheep. Scottish buyers didn't know the breed and were wary of them.

I took them all home again and was forced to fatten and sell them on the dead meat market through the spring and early summer. A slow maturing breed that needed about two months longer keep than Cheviots do, they competed for early grass with dairy cows. Any profit I made on the lambs was swallowed up by the extra cost of keeping the cows inside later than usual.

I never repeated the experiment, but because of it I had a far better understanding of the Welsh farmers' problems in trying to make a living with the only sheep breed suitable to their hills and climate.

Now, the new MP for Kincardine and Deeside will bring his own attributes and fresh talents to the job. But the farmers will find that he will need to be handled differently — just like my Welsh lambs.

Crowning glory!

I'm plagued by an ill-fitting bonnet.

Not a car bonnet, just an ordinary cloth cap. With a bonny blue and white check, it is smart enough, but it simply doesn't fit. Who could believe that size 7¼ would be just too small, yet 7⅜ far too big?

Anyway, this thing is an absolute pest. I was fencing by a busy roadside the other day, and every time I bent down to chap a staple in the low wires off went the bonnet amongst my feet.

Worse still, the wind caused by passing lorries carried it anything up to 20yd and I had to waste time retrieving it — usually from the opposite side of the fence, of course.

Maybe, as I grow scarcer of hair, my head is becoming skitey, preventing the bonnet from getting a decent grip. Still, my other ones fit all right.

My favourite is very old and disreputable, fit to be seen only in the milking parlour. Firmly clapped on my head, it is more for protection from you know what than for sartorial elegance.

It is the kind of bonnet you can see any day on country roads, perched squarely above a pair of specs, inside a very dirty, very slow-moving car. The eyes beneath the bonnet pay no attention to other road users because they are eagerly looking at what farmer neighbours are doing in their parks.

When the sun is troublesome, most motorists use their sun visors. A farmer uses his bonnet. Tractor cabs are fitted with sun visors nowadays, but they are very often stiff to adjust. The peak of a bonnet is more easily set at exactly the right angle.

My milking-parlour bonnet has been through the washing machine and out on the line so often that is has lost all its fooshin. It is a good job I have ears at each side of my head, otherwise I'd be permanently blinded by the all-enveloping headgear.

At the other end of the spectrum, I have a good bonnet — a going-ashore model that I use for marts or meetings. It fits comfortably and, as bonnets go, couldn't be smarter. A quiet blend of heather colours, it was made in Ireland from soft Connemara tweed. I gave myself a present of it during a visit to Eire some years ago.

The old offending piece of headgear is of a much harder material. It was manufactured in Yorkshire, where they obviously don't have heads exactly my size.

The bonnet has no warmth, although it does keep the wind from the increasingly-bare patch in the middle of my head.

A long immersion in the sheep dipper last year didn't help it. I had prepared the dipper (which is about 5ft deep) for giving 400 lambs their winter dip. On this occasion, I was the person standing in a hole at the side of the dipping bath, chest high to the edge, while two catchers presented the lambs backwards into the liquid.

We had no more than 20 sheep through when a maverick lamb jumped right over me and landed in the bath, taking my bonnet with it. The day was fine, so I worked on, bonnetless, until the job was done. Eventually, I fished one very dirty, smelly cap from the depths. It took many soakings in clean water to more or less eradicate the pungent smell of sheep dip.

I should have parted company with the bonnet at that time. However, I am a product of the hungry 30s and of wartime shortages. I was reared on: "waste not, want not!" And you'll never have to say: "I wish I had the bread that I once threw away". Clearly my thrift extends to bonnets as well as bread.

Many farm folk wear woollen tammies. I have tried one, but found that it kept me either too hot or too chilly when the wind sneaked through the knitting.

Since nobody wears hats to funerals these days, I suppose I could take on my redundant black homburg for work. However, maybe I would look too much like Albert Steptoe.

The best-fitting chapeau I ever owned was a lovely brown felt trilby of the kind sported by racehorse trainers. It was bought back in the days when there was money in farming, and I was extremely fond of it.

Sadly, the inevitable happened. One windy spring day when I was canvassing for votes near the mart in Thurso, a big lorry went past, creating a vortex. Off went my pride and joy, away up over the rooftops and out of sight. For all I know it is still orbiting somewhere around Dounreay.

I've tried tweed hats, deer-stalkers, fore and afts, luggit bonnets, balaclavas, souwesters, helmets — and managed to lose the lot.

I've never owned a bowler, but then I was never asked to judge a class at the Highland or Royal shows, where such headgear seems to be the obligatory uniform.

I have donned a top hat only once, and that was while sitting on the green benches in the House of Commons.

If a Member of Parliament wishes to address the Chair during a voting division, he must ask the Clerk of the House for a collapsable top hat, which that canny gentleman keeps in a handy drawer.

The MP is then obliged to wear the hat and remain seated while he speaks. Did you ever hear of anything so daft? And it doesn't happen only at panto time, mark you!

That silly top hat didn't fit me, either. Maybe I should go to the ships chandler at the harbour and try a yachting cap.

Surely it would withstand a blast of wind and still stay on the pow. Unlike this bloomin' nuisance of a thing . . .